Electrical properties

Advanced Physics Project for Independent Learning

Student's Guide

John Murray
in association with
Inner London Education Authority

How to use this student's guide

This is a programme for independent learning. It is not a textbook: it is a guide to using texts, experiments and other resources to help you to learn about important electrical concepts, electrical measurements and some of the uses of semiconducting materials.

There are sections of text in this guide which are to be read as in any other book, but much of the guide is concerned with helping you through activities designed to produce effective learning when you work independently. For a fuller explanation of the way APPIL is written you should read the *Student's Handbook*. What follows is a brief summary.

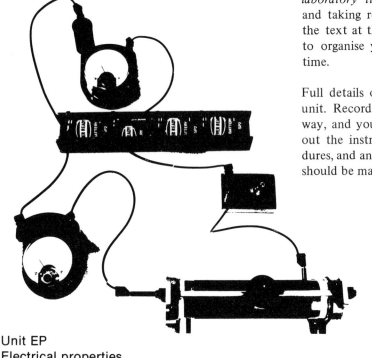

Objectives

What is to be learnt is stated at the beginning of each chapter – a general statement of what you will be doing, and more detailed objectives to be achieved. The objectives are particularly important, because they tell you what you should be able to do when you have finished working through the chapter, and so give you extra help in organising your learning. You will probably wish to refer to them when you have finished each chapter.

E Experiments

These are a very important part of the course. The experiments in each chapter are listed at the beginning of each chapter, with an indication of the approximate *laboratory time* required for setting up the apparatus and taking readings. Each experiment is referred to in the text at the most appropriate time. You should aim to organise your work so that it can be done at that time.

Full details of experiments are given at the end of the unit. Record your results, graphically or in some other way, and your conclusions. There is no value in copying out the instructions given, but notes on special procedures, and any details which might be useful for revision, should be made.

Q Self-assessment questions

These test your understanding of the work you have done, and will help you to check your progress. They are not intended to be difficult: you should be able to answer most of them quite easily. ■

The answers to self-assessment questions are given at the end of the book, but if you look at the answer before you have tried the question you will not be involved in the learning process and your learning may suffer.

Q Development questions

These are included to involve you in a proof or idea which is being developed in the text. ■

The answers to these questions are in the text or, for questions marked with an asterisk, at the end of the book. Involving yourself in the development helps you to learn: just looking at the answer is not so effective.

Q Study questions

For these you will need to use resources apart from this guide: for example, textbooks or experimental results. General references are given to basic books at the start of each chapter. You are not expected to consult all the references given, but you should always use more than one when possible. ■

This type of question usually requires longer answers than the others. These answers, in many cases, form a basis for your notes for the final examination and are therefore very important. Full answers are not usually given in this guide, though hints and partial answers are sometimes given (these questions are marked with an asterisk). Your answers to study questions should be handed in regularly for marking.

Use of resources

Background reading
This refers to books which are useful for a more detailed study of certain topics. They are also often interesting to read in their own right, and sometimes put the physics of the syllabus in its historical, social and technological context.

EXTENSIONS

Extensions are provided for several reasons.
(a) To provide additional material of general interest, e.g. applications.
(b) To provide more detailed treatment of some topics.
(c) To provide additional topics, or extensions of core material, to cover the requirements of a particular examination board. In this case, the section is marked SYLLABUS EXTENSION and will be essential study for some students, although others may find it of value. You should consult your teacher if you are not certain whether a particular syllabus extension is appropriate for you.

Questions on objectives

These are groups of questions which come at the end of each chapter, and are related to the objectives at the beginning of each chapter. Answering these will help you to tell whether you have achieved the objectives.

Organising your time

In this programme of work there is a variety of activities. Some of them, like experiments, need a laboratory, and you will also need to use the library. You must, therefore, organise your time so that you can make the best use of the resources available.

When you start a chapter, look through it and see what activities are included, then allocate each activity a time on your work schedule. Make sure, for example, that you do the experiments when you are timetabled in a laboratory. Follow the sequence in this guide if you can, but this may not always be possible.

In the introduction and at the beginning of each chapter, you will find the recommended time for completion of the work in each chapter. These times are given in units of one week. This assumes that you spend about 10 hours each week on physics, divided between class time, private study and home study. It is important to try to complete the unit in the stated time. The *progress monitor* will help you plan your time.

End-of-unit test

This is to enable your teacher to check the value of the course to you. You will be asked to do this test when you have completed the unit, and will be given details at the appropriate time.

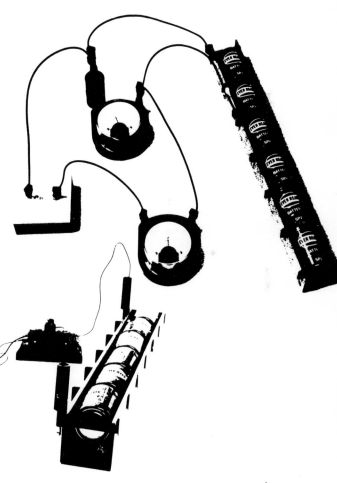

Introduction to the unit

In this unit you will be considering some of the principles which are necessary for understanding the applications of electricity.

As this unit is one of the recommended starting points for the course, there is a preliminary section, 'Starting block', which reviews some of your earlier physics studies which are relevant to this unit, and includes a preliminary test and advice on how to fill any gaps in your knowledge. Some of the topics covered in this unit are taken to A level standard: others will be developed in later units, and this is stated at appropriate points in the text.

Chapter 1 introduces a model which describes the conduction of electricity through solids and then revises and extends the concepts of electric charge, current, potential difference, resistance, power and energy.

Chapter 2 develops the principles and uses of some electrical measuring instruments. Section 2.1 considers the extension of the range of a moving-coil galvanometer as an ammeter or a voltmeter. This is essentially an application of the relationship between resistance, potential difference and current which was developed in chapter 1. Section 2.2 introduces the cathode ray oscilloscope. This is an important measuring and display instrument which you will be using throughout this course. The potentiometer and its applications are examined both theoretically and experimentally in sections 2.3 and 2.4. The final section is a SYLLABUS EXTENSION on the Wheatstone bridge circuit and its use for measuring resistance.

Chapter 3 is a SYLLABUS EXTENSION chapter on the conduction of electricity through liquids and gases. Section 3.1 revises and extends work on Faraday's laws of electrolysis and on the relationship between potential difference and current for electrolytes. It also includes an extension section on electric cells. The final part of the chapter deals briefly with the conduction of electricity through gases.

Chapter 4 provides an introduction to semiconducting materials and their application in electronic circuits. Section 4.1 explains the behaviour of n-type and p-type semiconducting materials in terms of valence electrons. The principles of the $p-n$ junction and the $n-p-n$ junction transistor are considered in sections 4.2 and 4.3. The chapter concludes with a consideration of the applications of the junction transistor as an amplifier and as a switch.

Recommended study times

You should spend about 6 to 7 weeks on this unit, as follows:

Chapter 1	1½ weeks	Chapter 3	½ week
Chapter 2	2½ weeks	Chapter 4	2½ weeks

Contents

Starting block

It is assumed in this unit that you have studied physics before, so the unit will build on and extend your present knowledge. Since you may have forgotten some of the things you learnt, or there may be a few things you are not sure about, this section is designed to help you to revise, re-learn or learn what you need to know to make the best use of this unit.

Start by reading the pre-requisite objectives: the things you need to be able to do before you begin work on the main part of the unit.

Then work through the preliminary test, which is based on the pre-requisite objectives. Work quickly through all parts of the test, without reference to books or to any other person (the aim is to check up on what you know now, so that you can find and fill up any gaps in your knowledge).

Mark your own test when you have finished, following the marking instructions. Read carefully through the comments.

When you have done this, you will be able to start chapter 1 with the confidence of knowing that you are ready to tackle new work.

Pre-requisite objectives

Before starting this unit you should be able to:

1   Use the following scientific terms correctly: conductor, insulator, electrolyte, conduction, ionisation, electron, positive ion, electron current, electric charge, electromotive force, potential difference, resistance, power, energy.

2   Recall the unit and standard symbol for each of the following physical quantities: current, electric charge, electromotive force, potential difference, resistance, power, energy.

3   Recall the relationship between current, potential difference and resistance.

4   Interpret simple circuit diagrams.

5   Recall an experiment to determine the resistance of a metallic conductor using an ammeter and a voltmeter.

6   Describe qualitatively the energy changes in an electric circuit which includes, for example, a battery, a resistance and a d.c. motor.

7   Solve electric circuit problems involving the following relationships:
electric charge = current × time
potential difference = current × resistance
electric power = current × potential difference
energy converted = power × time

Preliminary test

There are three types of question in this test, coded as follows.
MC   Multiple choice. Select the single best answer.
MR   Multiple response. Select all the correct answers.
NUM   Numerical answer. Work out the answer and write it down, including the unit where appropriate.

Part A   Scientific terms and units

Questions 1–4 *MC*
Which of the words (A–H) below best completes each of the sentences in questions 1–4?
A   conductor
B   electromotive force
C   electrons
D   insulator
E   positive ions
F   potential difference
G   protons
H   charge

1   Copper is a good _____ of electricity.

2   A positive ion is an atom or group of atoms which have lost one or more _____ .

3   An electric current is a movement of _____ .

4   The electric current in a metallic conductor at constant temperature is proportional to _____ .

Questions 5–10 *MC*

From the list of units (A–F) below, choose the correct unit for each of the quantities in questions 5–10.

A   coulomb
B   ampere
C   volt
D   ohm
E   joule
F   watt

5   Potential difference.

6   Energy.

7   Resistance.

8   Power.

9   Current.

10 Electric charge.

Part B   Current and charge

11 *MR*   Which of the following statements is/are correct?

A   1 coulomb = 1 ampere × 1 second

B   1 coulomb = $\dfrac{1 \text{ ampere}}{1 \text{ second}}$

C   1 ampere = 1 coulomb × 1 second

D   1 ampere = $\dfrac{1 \text{ coulomb}}{1 \text{ second}}$

Questions 12 and 13 *NUM*

The element of an immersion heater carries a current of 8.0 amperes.

12   How much electric charge passes a given cross-section in two minutes?

13   If the magnitude of the charge on an electron is 1.6×10^{-19} coulomb, how many electrons pass the cross-section in this time?

Questions 14–17 *NUM*

Circuit A in figure P1 shows one cell of negligible internal resistance connected in series with a lamp and an ammeter. The reading on the ammeter is 0.25 ampere.

In the circuits B–E similar lamps, ammeters and cells of negligible internal resistance are used.

14   In circuit B, what are the readings on ammeters A_1, A_2 and A_3?

15   In circuit C, what is the reading on ammeter A_4?

16   In circuit D, what are the readings on ammeters A_5 and A_6?

17   In circuit E, what are the readings on ammeters A_7, A_8 and A_9?

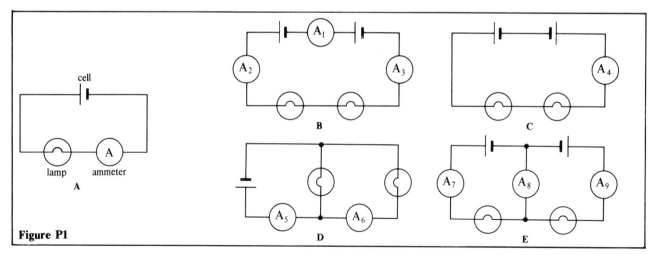

Figure P1

Part C Potential difference and current

18 *MC* Which of the circuits (A–E) in figure P2 is suitable for determining the resistance of the resistor X?

19 *MC* Figure P3 shows five graphs of potential difference against current. Which of the graphs (A–E) is correct if the resistor X is a metallic conductor whose temperature is kept constant?

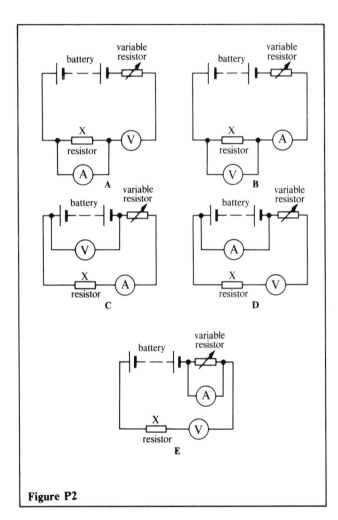

Figure P2

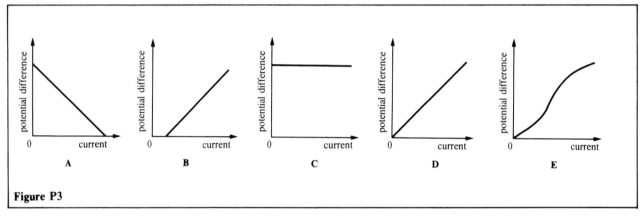

Figure P3

20 *MR* Which of the following statements is/are correct?

A   1 volt = 1 ohm × 1 ampere
B   1 ohm = 1 volt × 1 ampere
C   1 ampere = 1 volt × 1 ohm
D   1 ohm = $\dfrac{1\ \text{volt}}{1\ \text{ampere}}$

Questions 21 and 22 *NUM*
Consider the circuit shown in figure P4.

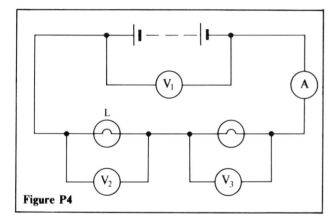

Figure P4

21 If the reading on the voltmeter V_1 is 20 volts, and that on V_2 is 12 volts, what is the reading on V_3?

22 If the reading on the ammeter is 0.25 ampere, what is the resistance of the lamp L?

23 *NUM* The current through a resistor of resistance 10 ohms is 0.5 ampere. What is the potential difference across the resistor?

24 *NUM* A potential difference of 240 volts is connected across an immersion heater of resistance 20 ohms. What is the current through the immersion heater?

25 *NUM* When a potential difference of 5.0×10^3 volts is applied across a resistor, the current through it is 2.0×10^{-4} ampere. What is the resistance of the resistor?

26 *NUM* A battery consisting of six cells, each of electromotive force 2.0 volts and negligible resistance, is connected across a resistor of resistance 24 ohms. What is the current through the resistor?

Part D   Electrical energy and power

27 *MR* Which of the following statements is/are correct?

A   1 watt = 1 ampere × 1 volt
B   1 watt = $\dfrac{1\ \text{volt}}{1\ \text{ampere}}$
C   1 ampere = 1 watt × 1 volt
D   1 volt = $\dfrac{1\ \text{watt}}{1\ \text{ampere}}$

Questions 28–30 *NUM*
An electric light bulb is marked 100 watts, 250 volts.

28 What is the current through the filament when the recommended p.d. is applied?

29 What is the resistance of the filament when in normal use?

30 How much heat and light energy is produced by the lamp in five minutes?

31 *MR* A battery is connected to a filament electric lamp, an electric motor and a switch as shown in figure P5. A load is attached via a pulley to the motor. Which of the energy changes (A–H) take place immediately after the switch is closed?

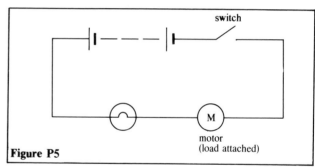

Figure P5

A   chemical energy to internal energy (heat)
B   chemical energy to kinetic energy
C   chemical energy to light energy
D   internal energy (heat) to light energy
E   kinetic energy to chemical energy
F   kinetic energy to potential energy
G   potential energy to internal energy (heat)
H   potential energy to kinetic energy

Marking

Compare your answers with those given below, and give yourself one mark for each fully correct answer. To be fully correct, only the one right answer should be given for multiple choice questions, all the right answers and no wrong ones for multiple response questions, and the unit as well as the number for numerical questions.

Add up your marks for each part of the test separately.

Answers

Part A *10 marks*

1 A
2 C
3 H
4 F
5 C
6 E
7 D
8 F
9 B
10 A

Part B *7 marks*

11 A, D (The charge that passes a given cross-section in a given time is equal to the product of the current and the time, i.e. charge = current × time.)
12 960 coulombs (2 × 60 × 8.0 coulombs)
13 6×10^{21} electrons
14 The readings on A_1, A_2 and A_3 are all 0.25 ampere. (The current in a series circuit is the same at all cross-sections. Charge does not get lost on its way around the circuit.)
15 A_4 reads zero. (The cells are connected in opposition, therefore the resultant electromotive force of the battery is zero. No net e.m.f., no current!)
16 A_5 reads 0.50 ampere and A_6 reads 0.25 ampere. (The potential difference, or voltage, across each lamp is the same and equivalent to one lamp across one cell, therefore a current of 0.25 ampere will pass through each lamp. The current through the battery and ammeter A_5 is thus 0.50 ampere.)
17 A_7 and A_8 both read 0.25 ampere. A_9 reads 0.50 ampere. (Consider the junction between ammeter A_9 and the two lamps. The total current passing into the junction is 0.25 ampere from the left and 0.25 ampere from the right. Thus, the current passing out is 0.50 ampere.)

Part C *9 marks*

18 B (The ammeter must be in series with the resistor X and the voltmeter in parallel with X.)
19 D (This is the only graph which shows a linear relationship between potential difference and current *and* passes through the origin. The potential difference is proportional to the current.)
20 A, D (The resistance of a conductor is the ratio of the potential difference across the conductor to the current through it, i.e.

$$\text{resistance} = \frac{\text{potential difference}}{\text{current}}.)$$

21 8 volts
22 48 ohms
23 5 volts
24 12 amperes
25 2.5×10^7 ohms
26 0.50 ampere (The total e.m.f. of the battery is 12 volts, so $I = 12/24$ A)

Part D *5 marks*

27 A, D (power = current × potential difference)
28 0.4 ampere
29 625 ohms
30 30 000 joules
31 A, B, D, F (Energy from the chemicals in the battery is transferred electrically to internal energy (heat) in the filament. Energy is also transferred to the rotating part of the motor as it speeds up and gains kinetic energy. The motor transfers energy mechanically so that the load is raised and gains gravitational potential energy.)

Using the test results

The pre-requisite objectives were tested as follows.

Objective 1   Throughout, particularly questions 1, 2, 3 and 4

Objective 2   Questions 5, 6, 7, 8, 9, 10, 11, 20 and 27

Objective 3   Question 19

Objective 4   Questions 14, 15, 16, 17 and 18

Objective 5   Question 18

Objective 6   Question 31

Objective 7   Questions 12, 13, 21, 22, 23, 24, 25, 26, 28, 29 and 30

Use the flowchart and your test result to see whether you need to do some follow-up work before starting chapter 1.

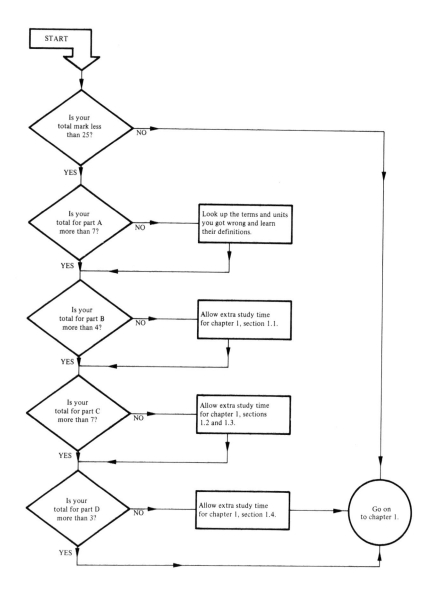

Chapter

Electric current

Aim

In this chapter you will look at how metals conduct electricity. You will also revise and develop the concepts of current, charge, electromotive force, potential difference, resistance, power and energy.

Objectives

When you have completed the work in this chapter you should be able to:

1   Use the following scientific terms correctly: conventional current, internal resistance.

2   Define and use the following scientific terms: electric charge, electromotive force (e.m.f.), potential difference (p.d.), resistance, conductance, resistivity, electrical conductivity, temperature coefficient of resistance, power, energy.

3   Define the following units: coulomb, volt, ohm, watt, joule.

4   Recall the unit and standard symbol for each of the following terms: resistivity, temperature coefficient of resistance.

5   Describe the motion of charge carriers in a metallic conductor and derive an expression for the electric current in terms of their drift velocity.

6   Distinguish between electromotive force and potential difference.

7   Distinguish between ohmic (linear) and non-ohmic (non-linear) devices.

8   State how the resistance of a piece of material depends upon its length and cross-sectional area.

9   Derive an expression for the combined resistance of two or more resistors in series and in parallel.

10 Show from first principles that the rate at which energy is dissipated in a resistor is proportional to the square of the current through it.

11 Recall that the rate at which energy is dissipated in an external circuit is a maximum when the external resistance is equal to the internal resistance of the source of electrical energy.

12 Solve electric circuit problems involving
(a) resistors in series and parallel,
(b) the relationships between potential difference, current, resistance, power, energy and time,
(c) the relationship between electromotive force, current and resistance for a complete circuit.

13 EXTENSION
State Kirchoff's rules and use them to solve electric circuit problems.

Experiments in chapter 1

EP 1   Investigating conductors
(1 hour)
EP 2   Effect of temperature on resistance
(½ hour)
EP 3   Internal resistance of a cell
(1 hour)

References

Bennet	Chapters 1 and 2
Brown	Chapters 1, 2 and 3
Duncan MM	Chapter 3
Nelkon	Chapter 33
Wenham	Chapters 24, 25, 26 and 27
Whelan	Chapters 48, 49 and 50

1.1 Current and charge

If you have not yet read the section 'How to use this student's guide', you should do so now.

Figure 1.1

We take electricity for granted, and rarely stop to think what happens when a switch is closed – or opened! We observe the *effects* of passing current through an electric circuit: a lamp lights up, a motor runs, and so on. We cannot see what is happening inside the filament of the lamp, or the wiring of the motor. We know that something is happening, but to explain the effects that we can observe we have to introduce concepts like energy, charge and potential difference, which are not observable.

Conduction of electricity through solids

We know when an electric current passes through a circuit, because we can observe its effects.

Q 1.1 Self-assessment question

There are three common effects of an electric current, each of which can be used as a basis for measuring current. What are they?■

Note. A self-assessment question is intended to help you to check your progress. You should be able to work through such a question quickly and get it right – without looking at the answer first! The answers to all self-assessment questions are given at the back of the book, so that you can confirm your answer after you have done the question.

To describe the mechanism of conduction, we have to form a picture or 'model' of what is happening at the level of atoms, molecules and ions.

Q 1.2 Study question

(a) In a typical metal, what is true of the outermost electron(s) of each atom? Explain why it makes sense to think of these as being 'shared' between all the ions in a piece of metal. How can the movement of these electrons be described? Why are they often referred to as 'free electrons'?

(b) When a potential difference is produced between the ends of a conductor an electric field is set up in it. Describe what effect this has on the motion of the free electrons, and explain why they do not get faster and faster. Why are the free electrons also called 'conduction electrons'?

(c) What happens to the energy transferred by the electric field to kinetic energy of these electrons? What observable change corresponds to this?

(d) What is meant by the 'drift velocity' of the conduction electrons? If we think of these electrons as being similar to the molecules of a gas, what does the drift velocity correspond to?■

Using references in answering a study question
References are given at the beginning of each chapter. Some are to general physics text books, others are to books concerned mainly with electricity. In all the references given you will find parts which are not relevant to a particular question. There are two ways of dealing with this efficiently.

1 Use the *index*. To do this, you will need to read through the question, decide what you want from the reference, and note the *key words*. Question 1.2, for example, is about the movement of electrons, and you will find index references to 'conduction electrons' or 'free electrons' in several books.

2 Use *sub-headings* to find relevant sections of the chapters. Read through these sections and make brief notes of the points you want to include in your answer.

For more help on how to make notes, consult the APPIL *Student's Handbook* and read the relevant chapter in *Use your head* by Tony Buzan.

Q 1.3 Self-assessment question

The conventional direction of an electric current, shown by an arrow on a circuit diagram (figure 1.2), is the direction in which *positive charge* would move if free to do so. The direction of flow of electrons is the opposite of this. Explain why.■

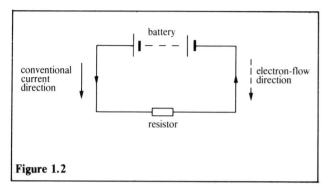

Figure 1.2

Q 1.4 Self-assessment question

The magnitude of the charge on the electron is 1.6×10^{-19} C. How many electrons are needed to carry a total charge of 1 C?■

Q 1.5 Study question

(a) Define the coulomb, the unit of electric charge, in terms of the ampere. (The ampere is the unit of current and is defined from the magnetic effect of an electric current. This is considered in the unit *Forces and fields*.)
(b) Write down the relationship between current, charge and time.■

Q 1.6 Self-assessment question

(a) What time is required to pass a charge of 3.6×10^4 C through an electroplating bath in which the current is 6.0 A?
(b) How many electrons per second pass through a cross-section of a conductor which carries a current of 3.2 A? (magnitude of charge on electron = 1.6×10^{-19} C)■

Drift velocity of electrons

Free electrons are accelerated by an electric field set up in a conductor. However, they progress through the conductor at a fairly steady average velocity. This velocity is limited because they are slowed down by constant collisions with positive ions.

An important and interesting question is 'how fast do these electrons move?' Before doing the next question, write down a guess at the average drift velocity of electrons in a typical piece of wire carrying a current of one ampere.

Q 1.7 Development question

In this question you will derive an expression for the mean drift velocity of the free electrons in a metallic conductor. Consider a metallic conductor (figure 1.3) of cross-sectional area A in which the free electrons are moving with an average drift velocity v. In a time t the electrons which pass through the section XY will have arrived at the section $X_1 Y_1$.
(a) Write down an expression for the distance through which the electrons have travelled in time t.
(b) Show that the number of electrons which passes through the section $X_1 Y_1$ in time t is $Anvt$, where n is the number of electrons per unit volume (the number density).

(c) The magnitude of the charge on each electron is e. Write down an expression for the charge that passes in time t.
(d) The current I through the conductor is equal to the rate of flow of charge. Show that the *mean drift velocity* of the electrons is given by

$$v = \frac{I}{nAe} \quad ■$$

Note. Answers to development questions are usually incorporated in the question or in the following text, though sometimes a suggested answer may be given at the back of the book.

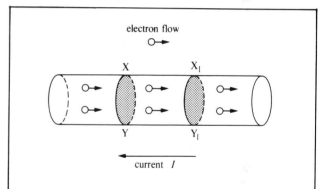

Figure 1.3 Electrons in a metallic conductor

We can now make an estimate for the mean drift velocity of electrons in a copper conductor by making some assumptions about the values of I, A and n. Suppose that there is one conduction electron for each atom of copper. Thus n will be numerically the same as the number of copper atoms in a cubic metre of copper.

Q 1.8 Development question
(a) Show that the number of atoms in a cubic metre of copper is approximately 10^{29}. The density of copper is 9.0×10^3 kg m^{-3}, and 63.5 kg of copper contains 6.0×10^{26} atoms of copper.
(b) Using the information from part (a) and the following data, show that the drift velocity of electrons in a copper conductor is approximately 10^{-4} m s^{-1}:
cross-sectional area of conductor = 1.0 mm^2 = 10^{-6} m^2
current = 1.0 A
magnitude of charge on the electron = 1.6×10^{-19} C. ∎

It is perhaps surprising that the charge carriers are moving very slowly. It would take an electron 10^4 s (approximately three hours) to travel a distance of one metre through such a copper conductor. Why then are the effects of the movement of charge, for example the heating of a lamp filament, observed almost instantaneously?

When a circuit is completed, an electric field is established in the conductor at a speed of over 10^8 m s^{-1}. This means that all the free electrons will experience a force, and hence be set into systematic drift motion, at almost exactly the same time wherever they are in the conductor.

The expression for the drift velocity of charge carriers has been derived by considering conduction through a metallic conductor. It also applies to the conduction of charge carriers in an electrolyte. In an electrolyte, the charge carriers are both positive and negative ions. These travel in opposite directions through the electrolyte in the presence of an electric field. (Chapter 3 considers conduction through liquids and includes experiment EP 11, which is an investigation of the mobility of these ions. You could do this experiment now.)

1.2 Electromotive force and potential difference

When an electric current passes through the filament of an electric lamp, there is an increase in the internal energy of the filament. This energy must be continuously supplied from a source, for example a battery or generator. A battery or generator is able to maintain one terminal positive (that is, it has a deficiency of electrons) and the other terminal negative (that is, with an excess of electrons). When it is connected to an external circuit, as shown in figure 1.4, an electric field is set up in the conductor which exerts a force on the electrons. As they move, the force does work on them. In this way, electric charge is moved around the circuit and energy is transferred from the source to other parts of the circuit. In practice, many generators produce alternating current (a.c.) rather than direct current (d.c.), but in broad terms the energy relationships are similar. (Alternating current is dealt with in the unit *Electromagnetism*.)

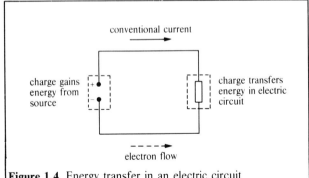

Figure 1.4 Energy transfer in an electric circuit

In order to explain what is happening in an electric circuit you must be familiar with the two concepts, *electromotive force* (e.m.f.), and *potential difference* (p.d.). The first concept, electromotive force, is concerned mainly with energy conversion within the *source*; the second, potential difference, with transfer of energy to the *external circuit*.

Electromotive force

Q 1.9 Study question*
What is the definition of electromotive force? State the unit in which it is measured. ∎

It is found by experiment that the energy drawn from an electrical source is proportional to the charge which flows. This means that each unit of charge is given the same amount of energy (for a given source). A torch battery which has an e.m.f. of 3.0 volts supplies 3.0 joules of energy to every coulomb of charge that passes through it. A power-station generator which has an e.m.f. of 25 000 volts will supply 25 000 joules per coulomb.

Q 1.10 Self-assessment question
If a charge Q passes through a source which has an e.m.f. E, write down an expression for the electrical energy W which is converted. ∎

Q 1.11 Self-assessment question
How much energy does a battery of e.m.f. 6.0 V supply
(a) when a charge of 5.0 C passes through it,
(b) when a current of 2.0 A flows for 10.0 s? ∎

Q **1.12 Self-assessment question**
A 12 V car battery is labelled 40 ampere hours. How much energy (in joules) can it convert?■

Potential difference

In the external circuit energy is available in various amounts to different parts of the circuit. The potential difference between two points in the external circuit tells us how much energy will be converted when unit charge passes between the points.

Potential difference is also measured in volts. A p.d. of three volts between two points means that three joules of electrical energy are converted into other forms of energy when one coulomb of electric charge passes between the points.

Q **1.13 Study question**
What is the definition of potential difference? Why is the unit of potential difference also the volt?■

Q **1.14 Self-assessment question**
(a) If a charge of Q passes between two points in a circuit between which there is a p.d. of V, write down an expression for the electrical energy W which is converted into other forms of energy.
(b) What is the p.d. between two points in a circuit if 400 J of electrical energy are changed to other forms of energy when 25 C of electric charge passes?■

1.3 Resistance

The conduction of electricity through a conductor was investigated experimentally in 1826 by the German scientist Georg Ohm. He found that for certain materials, metals in particular, there was a constant ratio between the current in a conductor and the potential difference applied across the conductor. This was true when the physical conditions were kept the same, particularly the temperature.

E **Experiment EP1**
Investigating conductors
In this experiment you will find out the effect of varying the p.d. across the terminals of several boxes, each of which contains a different conducting device.

Ohmic and non-ohmic conductors

Conductors can be divided into two groups: ohmic and non-ohmic. Ohmic conductors give a linear relationship between the applied potential difference and current (figure 1.5a). The resistance is constant, and reversing the p.d. gives the same value.

Q **1.15 Self-assessment question**
For ohmic conductors, the relation between current and p.d. is not merely linear, since the current is zero when the p.d. is zero. How can we describe the way in which current depends on p.d.?■

Non-ohmic conductors give a non-linear relationship between the applied potential difference and current (figure 1.5b). The resistance is variable. It may be quite different in the two directions.

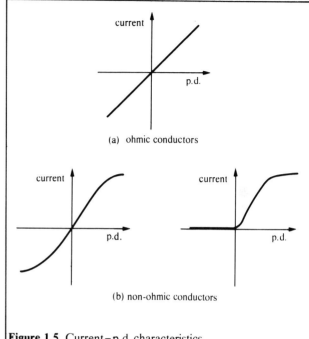

Figure 1.5 Current–p.d. characteristics

Q **1.16 Study question**
(a) Define electrical resistance.
•(b) State Ohm's law.
(c) Define the ohm, the unit of resistance.■

Q **1.17 Self-assessment question**
Two resistors of resistances 400 Ω and 100 Ω are connected in series to a supply of e.m.f. 240 V and negligible resistance. What is the p.d. across the 400 Ω resistor?■

Q 1.18 Study question

Explain, with the aid of diagrams, how a variable resistor can be used to control the current in a circuit (two different methods).■

The conductance G of a material is the reciprocal of its resistance:

$$\text{conductance} = \frac{1}{\text{resistance}}, \quad G = \frac{1}{R}$$

The unit of conductance, Ω^{-1}, is the Siemen, symbol S.

Resistor networks

Many electric circuits contain a network of resistors (figure 1.6). It is useful to be able to calculate the effective resistance of various combinations.

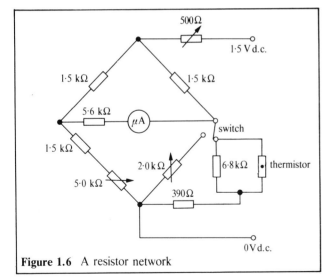

Figure 1.6 A resistor network

Q 1.19 Study question

(a) Show from first principles (that is, by considering p.d. and current) that the combined resistance R (figure 1.7) of three resistors of resistances R_1, R_2 and R_3, connected in series, is given by the relationship

$$\rightarrow \quad R = R_1 + R_2 + R_3$$

(b) Show from first principles that the combined resistance of the same three resistors, connected in parallel, is given by the relationship

$$\rightarrow \quad \frac{1}{R} = \frac{1}{R_1} + \frac{1}{R_2} + \frac{1}{R_3}$$

(c) Can your proofs be directly extended to a greater number of resistors in each case?■

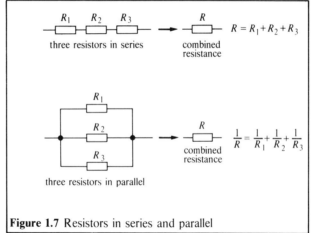

Figure 1.7 Resistors in series and parallel

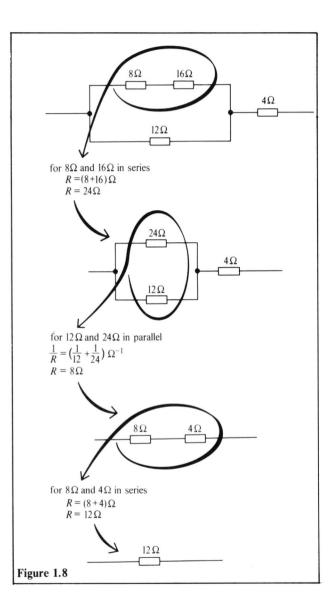

for 8Ω and 16Ω in series
$R = (8+16)\,\Omega$
$R = 24\,\Omega$

for 12Ω and 24Ω in parallel
$\frac{1}{R} = \left(\frac{1}{12} + \frac{1}{24}\right)\Omega^{-1}$
$R = 8\,\Omega$

for 8Ω and 4Ω in series
$R = (8+4)\,\Omega$
$R = 12\,\Omega$

Figure 1.8

Figure 1.8 shows how the combined resistance of a network that consists of series and parallel combinations can be obtained by applying the appropriate formula step by step. In all questions of this type, you should first plan the steps in tackling the problem.

Q **1.20 Self-assessment question**
Resistors of resistances 2 Ω, 4 Ω and 6 Ω are joined first in series and then in parallel. What is the combined resistance in each case?■

Q **1.21 Self-assessment question**
Calculate the combined resistance of the resistor network shown in figure 1.9.■

Factors which determine resistance

Resistors of many different types and values are needed in electric circuits (figure 1.10). For the construction of such resistors, it is necessary to know the factors which determine the resistance of a piece of material. To investigate these factors, the circuit shown in figure 1.11 can be used, with a wire made of the material that is being investigated connected between X and Y. The variable resistor keeps the current to a suitable value.

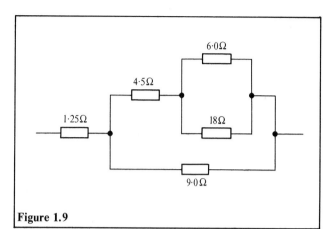

Figure 1.9

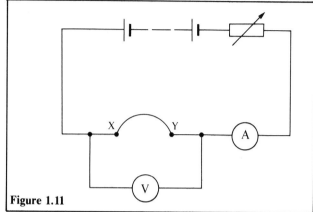

Figure 1.11

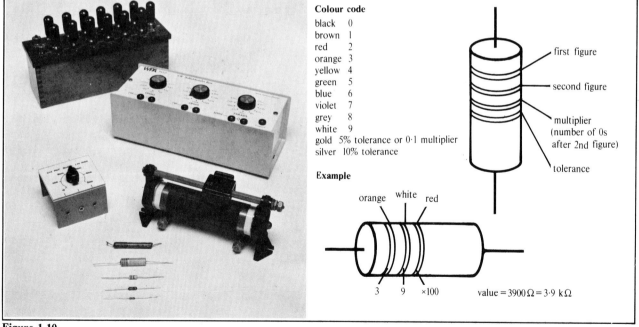

Figure 1.10

The results from such an experiment show that the resistance of a piece of material depends on three factors.

1   If the length l of the wire is increased, a *bigger* p.d. is required to drive the *same current* through the wire. More precisely, resistance is *proportional* to length, provided the cross-sectional area is constant.

$$R \propto l$$

2   If the cross-sectional area A of the wire is increased, a *smaller* p.d. is required to drive the *same current* through the wire. More precisely, resistance is *inversely proportional* to cross-sectional area, provided the length is constant.

$$R \propto \frac{l}{A}$$

3   The resistance depends upon the material.

These results can be summarised in the form of an equation:

➤ $R = \dfrac{\rho l}{A}$

where ρ is a property of the material called the *resistivity*.

Note. Resistivity refers to the material in general, (for example, copper), not just to a particular piece of it (for example, a wire).

Q 1.22 Self-assessment question
If all the linear dimensions of a piece of material were doubled, its resistance would

A   increase by a factor of 4.
B   increase by a factor of 2.
C   remain unchanged.
D   decrease by a factor of 2.
E   decrease by a factor of 4.∎

Q 1.23 Study question
(a) On theoretical grounds, using the results of the work on resistors in series and parallel, show that the relationships between resistance, length and cross-sectional area are to be expected.
(b) Define resistivity. Why is it an essential concept?
(c) Show that the unit of resistivity is the ohm metre (Ω m).
(d) Define the *conductivity* σ of a material and show that it has the unit seimen metre^{-1} (S m^{-1}).∎

Q 1.24 Self-assessment question
A wire used to make a heating element has a cross-sectional area of 0.80 mm^2, and the resistivity of the material is 5.0×10^{-7} Ω m. Calculate the length of wire which is required to make an element which has a resistance of 5.0 Ω.∎

EXTENSION

Q 1.25 Study question
An electrical strain gauge is a device which engineers can use to obtain information about the magnitude and distribution of strain in structures such as buildings, bridges and aircraft. Write brief notes on the way in which a mechanical strain in the gauge can cause a change in its resistance.∎

EXTENSION

The physical basis of Ohm's law

In section 1.1 an expression for the drift velocity v of charged particles in a conductor of cross-sectional area A carrying a current I was deduced:

$$v = \frac{I}{nAe} ,$$

where n is the number of free charge carriers per unit volume, or the number density, and e is the charge on each.

Suppose that the average drift velocity is proportional to the electric field strength E: $v \propto E$. The electric field is equal in size to the *potential gradient* along the conductor. (This is considered in the unit *Forces and fields*.)

If the length of the conductor is l and the p.d. across it is V, then (by definition)

$$\text{potential gradient} = \frac{V}{l}.$$

Therefore we may write

$$v = \frac{kV}{l}$$

where k is a constant and is numerically equal to the drift velocity for unit potential gradient.

Q 1.26 Study question

(a) Show that the resistance of a conductor is given by

$$R = \frac{l}{kneA}.$$

(b) Discuss the conditions under which the resistance of a conductor will be constant. ∎

Comprehension exercise

150 YEARS FROM OHM'S LAW

The delight of school teachers and the plague of pupils, crammed into minds late at night, written on the backs of hands, Ohm's Law should rank as one of the most widely remembered pieces of school physics. Ironically the discoverer, Georg Simon Ohm (1789–1854) was a school-teacher, but not by choice.

Bavarian by birth, Ohm came from a large family and received his early education at home from his father who was by profession a locksmith and whose bent for the sciences gave his sons an early aptitude in mathematics. When he was 11 Georg went to school and progressed from there to university in his home town of Erlangen. At 22 he graduated with a PhD and began to teach mathematics at the university. This was a poorly paid job with few prospects and, wanting more in life than this drudgery, Ohm became a school-teacher for the extra pay it offered. Although he hated it he stayed and when, in 1817, he got the chance to teach in a better school, the Jesuit School in Cologne, he took it. Here in the enthusiastic atmosphere of a newly founded school Ohm was stimulated and, as he had been asked to teach physics as well as mathematics, his interest began to shift more to the former.

He read avidly from the French classics of Lagrange, Legendre, Laplace, Biot, Poisson, Fresnel and Fourier, books whose abstruse mathematical style he was later to try to emulate. But the turning point came in 1820 when Oersted made his great discovery that an electric current flowing along a straight wire produces a magnetic field which will turn a compass needle held beneath it. The significance for Ohm was that it turned his mind to electricity. The school laboratory at Cologne was well equipped with apparatus and Ohm began to experiment.

However, it was not until 1825 that he got the idea of doing research with an eye to publication leading, he hoped, to recognition and an escape from the life of a school-teacher. The problem to which he addressed himself was to discover how the connecting wire between the two poles of a battery affected the current flowing through it. Ohm measured the current with a compass needle suspended by a thin torsion wire over a fixed straight portion of the circuit, an arrangement in direct descent from the classic experiments of Oersted and Coulomb, and one capable of great accuracy. When a current was flowing Ohm would adjust the twist in the torsion wire to give no deflection. The angle of twist was then a measure of the current.

At first Ohm used a voltaic pile as his source but it gave him a lot of trouble. Not only was there a current surge every time he connected it but the generation of gas in the pile reduced the current as the experiment proceeded. With much trouble Ohm managed to get consistent results which he published in 1825 and it was his editor who gave him a new and crucial idea. Poggendorf suggested he use Seebeck's recently discovered thermo-electric effect to generate the voltaic force as this would not change with time nor give current surges. Ohm started out again in 1826, the crucial year, to re-experiment using a thermocouple — this time with success.

Keeping one junction in ice and the other in boiling water, Ohm varied the length of wire x between the thermocouple terminals, measuring the current X each time. Ohm found that the equation which fitted his results was of the form $X = \frac{a}{x + b}$. By varying the thermocouple temperatures he found that a was proportional to the e.m.f. of the source, and b a constant for the source. In modern symbols we recognise this as the school-book formula $I = \frac{E}{R + r}$, with I the current, E the battery e.m.f., R the circuit resistance, and r the battery resistance. As he had so far used only one kind of wire of fixed diameter he went on to experiment with the dimensions and composition of the wire and found that its "resistance" varied in proportion to its length and inversely as its cross-sectional area with a constant factor dependent on its composition.

Failure in communication

Later, Ohm was offered sabbatical leave in Berlin which gave him a welcome relief from his teaching duties. Here Ohm wrote a book, in the style of the great French mathematicians, on the mathematical theory of the electric circuit. Published the following year, it contained no account of the experimental work from which it derived. Ohm was so influenced by those French texts that he failed to emphasise the practical aspects which might have brought him the early recognition he was seeking and deserved. The book fell on stony ground, its format and length disguising the simplicity of its message. As we shall see, when revealed and put to use by others, Ohm's Law was destined to become of enormous importance later in the century, both in the development of the telegraph and in the invention of the electric light bulb which shone the way to the "electric age". But Ohm never saw the full fruits of his discovery for he died in 1854. Only in the last 10 years of his life were honours bestowed on him by some of the world's scientific societies in recognition of his work. He finally attained a chair of physics at the University of Munich.

Ohm's work languished for almost 15 years before it received a staunch adherent in Charles Wheatstone, professor of physics at University College, London, who was quick to recognise its significance. It had been translated into English under the auspices of the British Association and published in 1841. Wheatstone was on the translation committee and must have been delighted to find that Ohm held the solution to his own problem, which was to find the best circuit configuration for producing electrical effects over long distances — the telegraph. He used the law to discover the best construction of battery and wires to produce a needle deflection at a given distance.

Wheatstone's first practical telegraph was set up parallel to Brunel's Great Western Railway from Paddington to West Drayton. By the 1850s the telegraph was a well established communication between major centres. However, the great challenge of the age was yet to come — the spanning of the Atlantic by telegraph cable. Ohm's seminal work was to show its influence here too. While the practical imagination was fired by the problem of finding a ship big enough to hold the cable, with landing gear strong enough to support two miles of cable dangling from ship to ocean bottom, the intellect of one man was stimulated to consider how an electric signal would pass through such a cable. This man was William Thomson (later Lord Kelvin). Thomson used the analogy between the flow of electricity and of heat to solve this problem, a comparison first recognised by Ohm, who had been greatly influenced by Fourier's book *The Theory of Heat* in writing about electricity.

The importance of the analogy is that for heat flow it is natural to include the storage of heat in the bar. Charge storage is just what is pronounced in the flow of electricity through a cable surrounded by water. So Thomson, using Fourier's equations, was able to solve the problem. He discovered that a sharp pulse dispatched from one end of the cable becomes spread out into a long slow quiver at the other, a fact which severely reduces the rate of sending if the received signals are not to overlap. The equations also told him that if the resistance of the cable is reduced the rate of sending can be increased. Therefore a scientific approach to cable design required pure copper in as thick a core as possible. Unfortunately the cable was already made and, when laid in 1858, was a failure. As Thomson's ideas became accepted he was able to influence the design of a second cable giving it three times as much copper per nautical mile as the first cable with proper choice of purity. This cable was laid by Brunel's great ship "The Great Eastern" and completed in 1866. It was a success. Within 24 hours of connection the line was at capacity with messages to and from the New World.

More practical applications

The telegraph obtained its electric power from batteries, that is from chemical reactions, but in 1831 Michael Faraday had made the momentous discovery that electricity could be generated mechanically. It was a discovery that remained under-developed for many years for, although electricity had many uses, none of these was so universal as to augur a return on investment in development. It was Edison, a great admirer of Faraday, who perceived that if a profit were to be made it would be necessary not only to develop an efficient dynamo but also to create an electrical distribution system and a universal use for electricity. For Edison that meant the electric light bulb and, possessed of the imagination and initiative necessary to develop the complete system, he started work.

Once he had grasped the idea Edison was guided in his calculations by Ohm's Law. First, since each light must be independent, the bulbs would be wired in parallel — a departure from the arc-light practice of the time. Secondly, he calculated the weight of copper in the wires necessary to light a given housing area with lamps of one ohm resistance each, a typical value for lamps being patented at this time by others. The result was impossibly expensive. He then did the calculation with hundred ohm lamps and the system began to look feasible. This then was the crux, a high-resistance lamp filament was needed. Edison, directing his research team at Menlo Park set out to find a suitable filament. They concentrated on carbon which has inherent high resistivity, and on making the filament as thin as possible consistent with strength and long life. When they finally succeeded, Edison and his workers just sat watching the filament blaze for its record 40-hour duration. That was in 1879. Three years later, when Edison started up the steam engines at the Pearl St. generator in New York City and the electric light shone in distant offices, the electric age had begun.

Electrical science in the 19th century was dominated by materials which obeyed Ohm's Law but the 20th century has seen the development of circuitry far from ohmic in its operation. The starting point was again the light bulb and Edison.

One of the problems with the carbon filament lamps was that, after a time, the glass became blackened and this so reduced the lamp life that Edison became interested. He noticed that the black shadow of carbon contained one clear line in the shape of the projection of one side of the filament. It appeared therefore that carbon was being emitted by only one side of the filament loop, the negative side. The "Edison effect" remained unexplained until the discovery of the electron which, emitted from a negative hot wire, travels freely in a vacuum, in straight lines.

Thus the triumph of the application of Ohm's Law in the 19th century, the light bulb, provided the link with the new "bulbs" of the 20th century. First the valve, giving us the radio, and then the cathode ray tube for television, not to mention the insides of pocket calculators or computers which owe everything to the transistor whose electrical properties are certainly a long way on from Ohm.

(Article by Christopher Farrell from *New Scientist*, 30th September, 1976.)

Questions

1   What problems did Ohm have to overcome in doing his experiments? How did he overcome them?

2   Why did he omit his experiments from the book that he wrote? Why are experiments important in physics?

3   Explain why the mathematical relationship found by Ohm was essential to the development of (a) the telegraph; (b) the electric light bulb.

4   Write a brief summary of the article to emphasise how Ohm's work is typical of any advance in physics.

The effect of temperature on resistance

E **Experiment EP 2**
Effect of temperature on resistance
In this experiment you are required to find out how temperature affects the ability of a material to conduct electricity. You are not required to make a detailed investigation, but from your observations find the way in which the resistance of the material is affected by temperature. You will investigate three materials, a coil of copper wire, a carbon resistor and a thermistor (this is a device made from a semiconducting material).

The way in which resistance varies with temperature can be described by the *temperature coefficient of resistance*. In the case of metals (over a wide range of temperature) the variation is approximately linear (figure 1.12). It can be represented by the equation

➜ $R = R_0 (1 + a\,\theta)$

where R_0 is the resistance at $0\,°C$, R is the resistance at temperature θ, θ is the change in temperature from $0\,°C$ and a is the temperature coefficient of resistance.

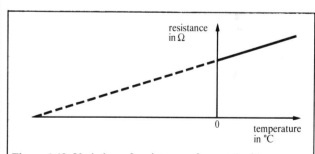

Figure 1.12 Variation of resistance of a metal with temperature

Q **1.27 Study question**
(a) Show that:

$$a = \frac{R - R_0}{R_0 \theta}$$

(b) Define in words the temperature coefficient of resistance and show that its unit is $°C^{-1}$ or K^{-1}. (K stands for kelvin, a unit of temperature which is introduced in the unit *Structure of matter*.)■

Q **1.28 Self-assessment question**
A coil of copper wire has a resistance of 30 Ω at 20 °C. Calculate its resistance at 100 °C, if the temperature coefficient of resistance of copper is $4.0 \times 10^{-3} °C^{-1}$. (Hint: write down two equations and eliminate R_0.)■

Q **1.29 Self-assessment question**
Measurements of potential difference and current on three different devices gave the graphs A, B and C (figure 1.13). Explain how the *resistance* of each device depends upon the p.d. which is applied, and suggest what each device might be.■

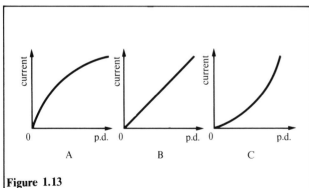

Figure 1.13

Internal resistance
When a battery (or other source of e.m.f.) supplies a current, the potential difference across the terminals of the battery falls.

Q **1.30 Development question***
A battery of four 1.5 V cells in series, each of resistance 0.5 Ω, is connected to a resistor of resistance 10 Ω. The current is allowed to pass for 20 s. Calculate:
(a) the total e.m.f. of the battery,
(b) its effective internal resistance,
(c) the total resistance of the circuit,
(d) the current through the circuit,
(e) the p.d. across the 10 Ω resistor,
(f) the charge that flowed through the circuit,
(g) the energy supplied by the battery,
(h) the energy used in heating the resistor.

Explain why the p.d. across the resistor is less than the e.m.f. of the cell.■

Q **1.31 Development question***
The circuit equation for a complete circuit can be derived by applying the principle of conservation of energy. Figure 1.14 shows a circuit in which a battery of e.m.f. E and internal resistance r is connected to part of the circuit which has an effective resistance R. The p.d. across R is V, and the current through the circuit is I. In a given time, a charge of Q flows past each cross-section of the circuit.
(a) Write down expressions for (i) the energy supplied by the battery, and (ii) the energy dissipated in the external circuit.
(b) The p.d. across the internal resistance is v, and the energy dissipated in the internal resistance is vQ. Show that $E = V + v$, and explain this equation in words.
(c) Using the relationships $V = IR$ and $v = Ir$, show that

→ $E = I(R + r)$.

This is the circuit equation for a complete circuit.
(d) In an experiment to determine the internal resistance of a cell, a series of values for the current I through a resistor and the corresponding p.d. V across the resistor were obtained. From these results, a graph of V (y axis) against I (x axis) was plotted. Sketch the shape of the graph and explain how the e.m.f. of the cell and the internal resistance can be found from the graph. (Hint: obtain a relationship between V, I, E and r in the form $y = mx + c$.)■

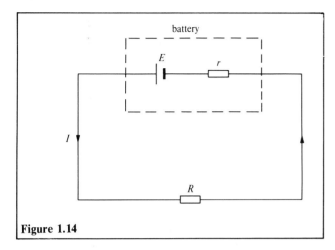

Figure 1.14

E Experiment EP 3
Internal resistance of a cell

In this experiment you will use a high-resistance voltmeter to measure the p.d. across the terminals of a cell in two different circumstances. First you will measure it on open circuit, when no current is passing. Then you will measure the p.d. across the cell when the cell is delivering a current to an external load. From your measurements you will obtain a value for the internal resistance of the cell.

Q 1.32 Self-assessment question
A torch bulb is marked 2.5 V and 0.3 A. When it is connected to a dry battery of e.m.f. 3.0 V the correct p.d. of 2.5 V is produced across it. Calculate the internal resistance of the battery.■

Q 1.33 Self-assessment question
(a) Under what conditions will the e.m.f. of a source be equal to the p.d. across its terminals?
(b) Under what conditions will the p.d. be half the e.m.f.?■

Worked example
Four cells, each of e.m.f. 1.5 V and internal resistance 0.5 Ω are connected to a parallel combination of two resistors of resistances 2.0 Ω and 3.0 Ω, in series with a 1.8 Ω resistor. Calculate
(a) the current passing through the 1.8 Ω resistor,
(b) the potential difference across the terminals of the battery.

The circuit diagram is shown in figure 1.15.
Total e.m.f. of the battery = 6.0 V.
Total internal resistance = 2.0 Ω.
External resistance = 1.8 Ω + 1.2 Ω = 3.0 Ω.
Total resistance of the circuit = 5.0 Ω.
Current through 1.8 Ω resistor = 1.2 A.
Potential difference across the terminals of the battery = 3.6 V.

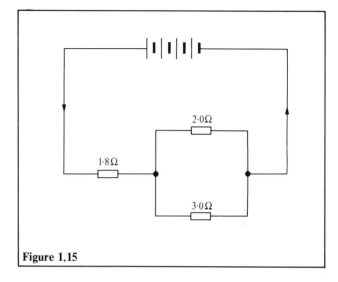

Figure 1.15

Q 1.34 Self-assessment question
A battery which consists of six cells in series, each of e.m.f. 1.5 V and internal resistance 0.5 Ω, is connected to two 3.0 Ω resistors which are in parallel. Calculate:
(a) the current through each resistor,
(b) the p.d. across the terminals of the battery.■

Q 1.35 Self-assessment question
When an accumulator is connected directly to a steady d.c. supply of 2.5 V and negligible resistance, the charging current is found to be 0.5 A. When the terminals of the same accumulator are connected to a 7.6 Ω resistor, the discharge current is 0.25 A. Calculate the e.m.f. and internal resistance of the accumulator. (Hint: when an accumulator (lead–acid battery) is being charged, its positive terminal is connected to the positive terminal of the supply.)■

1.4 Electrical energy and power

We know that when an electric current passes through a circuit, energy from the source (battery) is available elsewhere. If the external circuit is a resistor, then energy is dissipated as internal energy. The rate at which a device transfers or converts energy is known as its *power*, P. The unit of power is the watt.

Q 1.36 Self-assessment question
How is the watt related to the joule?■

Q 1.37 Self-assessment question
A current of 2.0 A passes through a 5.0 Ω resistor. Calculate:
(a) the p.d. across the resistor,
(b) the electric charge which passes any cross-section in 10 s,
(c) the energy dissipated as internal energy in the resistor,
(d) the rate at which energy is dissipated.■

Q 1.38 Development question*
In this question you will derive a general expression for the rate at which energy is dissipated as internal energy in a resistor. A resistor of resistance R carries a current I for a time t. The potential difference across the resistor is V. This p.d. V is numerically equal to the energy which is transferred when a charge of one coulomb passes between the points A and B (figure 1.16).
(a) How much energy is transferred when a charge Q passes between the points A and B?

(b) Current is the rate of flow of charge, that is

$$charge = current \times time$$
$$Q = I\,t.$$

Show that the rate at which energy transfer takes place is given by

➡ $P = I\,V.$

(c) Show that $P = I^2 R$. Write a statement of this equation in words (this equation is sometimes referred to as Joule's law).■

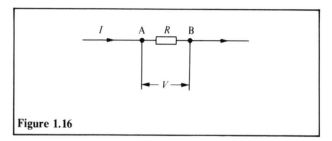

Figure 1.16

Q 1.39 Self-assessment question
The commercial unit of electrical energy is the kilowatt hour. How many joules are there in a kilowatt hour?■

Q 1.40 Self-assessment question
(a) What is the resistance of a 240 V, 60 W electric light bulb when in use? When a student measured the resistance using a dry cell and a milliammeter the result was 190 Ω. Why are the two answers different?
(b) A p.d. of 4.0 kV is applied across a resistor of 20 MΩ. What is the power dissipated?
(c) Estimate the energy stored in a 1.5 V dry cell, and hence calculate the cost of a kilowatt hour of energy in this form. Compare it with the cost of energy from the electric mains supply.■

Energy transfer in an electric circuit

In the electric circuit shown in figure 1.17 there are two main parts:
(a) the device (battery or generator) which supplies energy (often called the source);
(b) the device (resistor, motor, etc.) which transfers energy to some other part of the system (often called the load).

In each case the energy transferred can be calculated from a knowledge of the potential difference V across the device, the current I in the circuit and the time t.

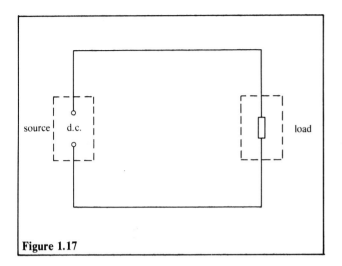

Figure 1.17

Q 1.41 Development question*
(a) By applying the circuit equation $E = I(R + r)$, and using $V = IR$, show that

$$EIt = VIt + I^2 rt.$$

(b) What do the terms EIt, VIt and $I^2 rt$ represent?■

Maximum power

In a circuit the internal energy that is dissipated in the source is not useful. Often we need to know how to get the maximum power supplied to the load. This has applications to hi-fi equipment and in telecommunications such as telephone circuits and TV.

Q 1.42 Development question*
An energy source which has an e.m.f. E and internal resistance r is connected to a resistive load of resistance R. Using equations already derived, show that the rate at which energy is transferred to the load is given by

$$P = \left(\frac{E}{R + r}\right)^2 R.\;■$$

Q 1.43 Development question*
An energy source which has an e.m.f. of 4.0 V and internal resistance 2.0 Ω is connected to a load which has a resistance which can be varied.

The following table of results has been obtained by calculating the current I for a certain value of load resistance R, then calculating the power dissipated in the load.

resistance R/Ω	0	0.5	1.0	2.0	3.0	4.0	5.0	6.0
power P/W	0	1.3	1.8	2.0	1.9	1.8	1.6	1.5

(a) Plot a graph to show how the power that is delivered to the load varies with the resistance of the load.
(b) What is the resistance of the load when the power has a maximum value?
(c) How is this resistance related to the internal resistance of the energy source?■

Q 1.44 Self-assessment question
A source having an e.m.f. 240 V and internal resistance 400 Ω supplies a current to a load which has resistance R. Calculate the p.d. across the load resistor, the current, and the power delivered to it, for each of the following values of R: 20 Ω, 400 Ω, 8 000 Ω. Comment on your results.■

From these questions you can see that the power delivered to the load is a maximum when the resistance of the load and that of the source are equal. (It is possible to show this theoretically from the equation in question 1.42.) When a circuit is connected in such a way the source and the load are said to be *matched*.

EXTENSION

Q 1.45 Study question
Use differential calculus to show that the power delivered to the load is a maximum when the resistances of the load and source are equal. (Hint: differentiate the expression

$$P = \left(\frac{E}{R + r}\right)^2 R$$

with respect to R, and equate to zero.)■

1.5 Kirchhoff's rules

The analysis of circuit problems can be reduced to the application of two standard rules, called Kirchhoff's rules.

Conservation of charge

The charge flowing into a junction equals the charge flowing out in the same time. Net charge cannot disappear, nor can it appear from nowhere. Applying this to figure 1.18,

$$I_1 = I_2 + I_3$$

or $\quad I_1 - I_2 - I_3 = 0.$

Currents *into* the junction are I_1, $-I_2$ and $-I_3$, so we can write

$$\Sigma I = 0 \qquad\qquad Rule\ 1$$

Note: Σ means 'the sum of', with the signs taken into account.

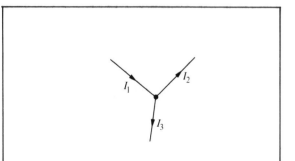

Figure 1.18 Kirchoff's first rule

Conservation of energy

If we consider a complete circuit, the energy taken from the source is equal to the energy distributed in the whole circuit in the same time. Applying this to figure 1.19, if Q is the charge flowing past each cross-section of the circuit in a given time,

$$E Q = (IR)\,Q + (Ir)\,Q$$
so $\quad E = IR + Ir,$ for this simple case.

In general,

$$\Sigma E = \Sigma IR \qquad\qquad Rule\ 2$$

This is called the *loop equation*. It can be applied to any loop in a circuit, if the signs are taken into account.

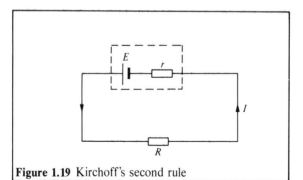

Figure 1.19 Kirchoff's second rule

Q **1.46 Study question**
State Kirchhoff's rules in words.■

Q **1.47 Self-assessment question**
Two batteries of negligible resistance are connected to three resistors, as shown in figure 1.20.
(a) Calculate the current through each of the resistors.
(b) Repeat the calculation with the battery E_2 reversed.■

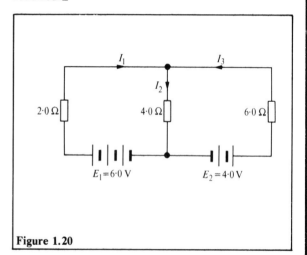

Figure 1.20

Questions on objectives

Before you attempt these, check through the list of objectives for this chapter and make sure that your notes on the chapter have not left out anything important.

1 Define resistivity, ρ. Illustrate your definition with a diagram and give the relevant equation, naming symbols and their usual units.

(objectives 2, 4 and 8)

2 Express the following units in terms of the units of the fundamental quantities, mass (kg), length (m), time (s), and current (A):
(a) coulomb
(b) joule
(c) volt
(d) ohm.

(objectives 2 and 3)

3 Define the volt. Explain the difference between electromotive force and potential difference.

(objectives 3 and 6)

4 (a) Describe qualitatively how electrical conduction in a metal may be explained in terms of a simple free-electron model.
(b) State what quantities you would need to know in order to calculate the mean drift velocity of electrons in a conductor which carries a current.

(objective 5)

5 Give an example of a conducting device which does not obey Ohm's law. Sketch a graph to represent the current – potential difference relationships for the device and point out the feature(s) of the graph which indicate that Ohm's law is not obeyed.

(objective 7)

6 Derive an expression for the combined resistance of two resistors, of resistances R_1 and R_2, connected in parallel.

(objective 9)

7 A cylindrical wire of radius r, length l and resistivity ρ carries a current I. Show that the rate at which energy is dissipated is given by:

$$P = \frac{I^2 \rho l}{\pi r^2}.$$

(objectives 8 and 10)

8 A battery is connected in series with a 6.0 Ω resistor and a switch. A high resistance voltmeter is connected across the battery and reads 4.5 V when the switch is open and 3.0 V when the switch is closed.
(a) What is the e.m.f. of the battery?
(b) Calculate the internal resistance of the battery.

(objective 12)

9 Two resistors of 6.0 Ω and 12.0 Ω are connected in parallel across a battery of e.m.f. 12 V and negligible internal resistance. Calculate:
(a) the current through each resistor,
(b) the power supplied by the battery,
(c) the equivalent resistor R which can replace the 6.0 Ω and 12.0 Ω resistors in parallel.

(objective 12)

10 (a) A wire which is used to make a heating element has a resistivity of 5.0×10^{-7} Ω m and cross-section 0.8 mm². Calculate the length of wire required to make up a 250 V, 1000 W element.
(b) If there are 8×10^{28} conduction electrons in every cubic metre of wire, calculate the mean drift velocity of the electrons in the wire when the 250 V p.d. is applied (assume this to be d.c.).
(magnitude of charge on electron is 1.6×10^{-19} C)

(objectives 5, 8 and 12)

Compare the time you took to complete this chapter with the recommended time. Are you keeping up to schedule?

Chapter 2

Electrical measurements

Aim

The aim of this chapter is to help you grasp the principles of several sorts of electrical measurement, and to learn how to select appropriate measuring instruments for use in a given situation.

Objectives

When you have completed the work in this chapter, you should be able to:

1 Use the following scientific terms correctly: thermoelectric effect, thermoelectric e.m.f., thermocouple, shunt, multiplier.

2 Describe and explain how a galvanometer can be modified to measure a wide range of currents and potential differences.

3 Describe and explain how to use a cathode ray oscilloscope
(a) to measure potential difference,
(b) to measure frequency and intervals of time,
(c) as a display device.

4 Describe the construction and the principle of operation of the potentiometer.

5 Perform and describe experiments, using a potentiometer, to determine:
(a) the electromotive force and internal resistance of a source of electrical energy, for example, a battery;
(b) the current passing through a given resistor;
(c) the resistance of a given resistor;
(d) a small potential difference, for example, a thermoelectric e.m.f.

6 Explain how the results of the experiments listed in objective 5 can be used to calculate the appropriate physical quantities.

7 Solve problems from first principles involving the following:
(a) shunts (parallel resistors) and multipliers (series resistors);
(b) the use of the potentiometer.

8 EXTENSION
Describe the construction and principle of the Wheatstone bridge circuit.

9 EXTENSION
Perform and describe an experiment, using a metre bridge, to determine resistance.

10 EXTENSION
Solve problems on the Wheatstone bridge circuit.

Experiments in chapter 2

EP 4 The cathode ray oscilloscope
(1 hour)
EP 5 The potentiometer
(1 hour)
EP 6 Internal resistance of a cell using a potentiometer
(1 hour)
EP 7 Measuring resistance with a potentiometer
(1 hour)
EP 8 Thermoelectric e.m.f. and temperature
(1 hour)
EP 9 EXTENSION
Measuring resistance with a metre bridge
(¾ hour)
EP 10 EXTENSION
Temperature coefficient of resistance (optional)
(1 hour)

References

Bennet   Chapters 4, 8 and 13
Brown   Chapters 3, 4 and 11
Duncan MM   Chapter 3
Nelkon   Chapters 33, 34 and 41
Wenham   Chapters 27, 29 and 43
Whelan   Chapters 51, 54 and 60

Chapter 2

Study time: 2½ weeks

2.1 Ammeters and voltmeters

In this section we shall consider methods of measuring current, potential difference and resistance. The magnitude of a current can be determined by measuring its magnetic effect; heating effect or chemical effect. We shall be concerned with instruments which depend on the magnetic effect and, in particular, with the way in which the moving-coil galvanometer can be adapted to measure current (an ammeter) and potential difference (a voltmeter).

The moving-coil galvanometer

A galvanometer is a sensitive instrument which can be used to detect very small currents. The moving-coil galvanometer (one version of which is illustrated in figure 2.1), consists of a coil of copper wire which is wound on a metallic frame and suspended or pivoted between the poles of a permanent magnet. It is usually designed so

Figure 2.1

that the deflection of the coil is directly proportional to the current. (The construction and principle of operation of the moving-coil galvanometer is considered in more detail in the unit *Forces and fields*.) In potentiometer and bridge circuits it is used to indicate that no current is flowing in part of the circuit. It is then said to be used as a null indicator.

Q **2.1 Self-assessment question**
Why is the accuracy of calibration of a null indicator unimportant?■

Current sensitivity

The *current sensitivity* of an instrument indicates the deflection that is produced by unit current. Sometimes the reciprocal of this, the current required to give unit deflection, is used, but this should not strictly be called the sensitivity.

Current sensitivity S is defined by the equation

$$S = \frac{\theta}{I}$$

where θ is the deflection produced by a current I. The unit of current sensitivity is the radian per ampere, rad A^{-1}. It is also sometimes expressed in terms of divisions per ampere or millimetres per ampere. In practice, currents of the order of amperes are not passed through galvanometers of this type, and you will usually find the values quoted in terms of milliamperes (or microamperes).

Q **2.2 Self-assessment question**
A 5.0 Ω resistor is connected in parallel with a galvanometer of resistance 95 Ω. This combination is then joined in series with a 2.0×10^4 Ω resistor and a battery of e.m.f. 2.0 V. If the deflection is 50 divisions, calculate the sensitivity of the galvanometer in divisions per microampere.■

Ammeters

An ammeter (figure 2.2) is used to measure a much larger current than a galvanometer.

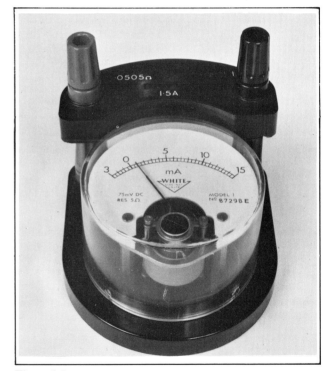

Figure 2.2

Q **2.3 Study question**
  How can a galvanometer be converted into an ammeter? Include in your answer a circuit diagram, an explanation of the word 'shunt' and a comment on the relative values of the resistances of the galvanometer and shunt.■

The following example illustrates how the range of the meter can be varied.

Worked example
A moving-coil galvanometer of resistance 5.0 Ω requires a current of 0.01 A to produce full-scale deflection. How can it be converted into an ammeter reading 0–10 A?

The galvanometer is converted by connecting a resistance in parallel such that when the total current is 10.0 A, the current for full-scale deflection goes through the coil and the rest passes through the shunt (figure 2.3). Because the coil and resistance are in parallel, the p.d. across each is the same:

  p.d. across coil = p.d. across shunt.
Using $V = IR$,
  $0.01 \text{ A} \times 5\ \Omega = 9.99 \text{ A} \times R_S$
where R_S is the resistance of the shunt.

$$R_S = \frac{0.05 \text{ A } \Omega}{9.99 \text{ A}} = 0.005\,005\ \Omega$$

A resistance of 0.005 005 Ω must be placed in *parallel* with the galvanometer to convert the galvanometer into an *ammeter* with a maximum deflection of 10.0 A.

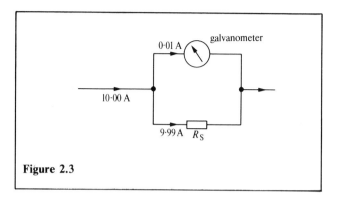

Figure 2.3

Q **2.4 Self-assessment question**
  Explain why the resistance of an ammeter should always be low. What would be the effect if an ammeter had an appreciable resistance?■

Q **2.5 Self-assessment question**
  A milliammeter has a resistance of 5.0 Ω and gives full-scale deflection for a current of 15 milliamperes. How would you adapt it so that it could be used as an ammeter reading to 1.5 A?■

Voltmeters
A voltmeter (figure 2.4) is used to measure the potential difference between two points.

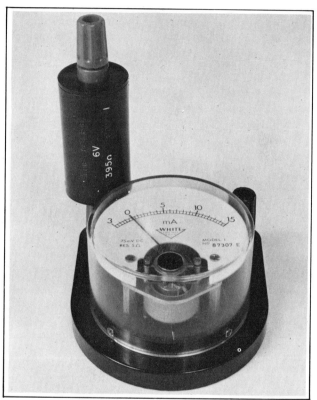

Figure 2.4

Q **2.6 Study question**
  How can a galvanometer be converted into a voltmeter? Your answer should include a circuit diagram, an explanation of the word 'multiplier' and an indication of the relative magnitudes of the resistances involved.■

The following example illustrates how the range of the meter can be varied.

Worked example
A moving-coil galvanometer of resistance 5.0 Ω requires a current of 0.01 A to produce full-scale deflection. How can it be converted into a voltmeter reading 0–10 V?

The galvanometer is converted by connecting a resistance R in series with the coil, such that the current for full-scale deflection will produce a p.d. across the coil and resistor equal to the maximum to be measured (figure 2.5).

Using $V = IR$,
$$10 \text{ V} = 0.01 \text{ A } (R + 5 \text{ }\Omega)$$
$$R = 995 \text{ }\Omega$$

A resistance of 995 Ω must be placed in *series* with the galvanometer to convert the galvanometer into a *voltmeter* with a maximum deflection of 10 V.

An alternative approach is as follows:
The p.d. across the coil which gives full-scale deflection is 0.05 V. The total p.d. is 10.0 V, which is 200 times as much. So the total resistance must be 200 times the coil resistance (5.0 Ω), that is, 1000 Ω. Hence, the resistance of the multiplier is (1000 − 5) Ω, giving 995 Ω.

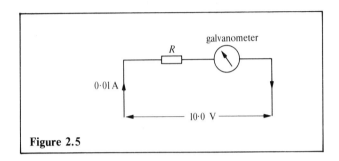

Figure 2.5

Q 2.7 Self-assessment question
Explain why a 'good' voltmeter should have a high resistance. What would be the effect if a voltmeter had only a moderate resistance (assuming it could still indicate the appropriate p.d.)?■

Q 2.8 Self-assessment question
The full-scale deflection of a moving-coil galvanometer of resistance 5.0 Ω is 2.0 mA. How can it be adapted to measure a maximum p.d. of 100 V?■

Q 2.9 Self-assessment question
Two resistors of 500 Ω and 2000 Ω in series are connected to a 100 V supply.
(a) Calculate the p.d. across each resistor.
(b) What will be the reading on a voltmeter of resistance 2000 Ω when placed across first the 500 Ω resistor, then the 2000 Ω resistor?
(c) Comment on the significance of your results.■

Q 2.10 Self-assessment question
You are required to design a voltmeter, range 0–25 V, and have two meters, A_1 and A_2, available. A_1 is a milliammeter of resistance 5 Ω and full-scale deflection 10 mA. A_2 is a microammeter of resistance 50 Ω and full-scale deflection 100 μA. Which meter, A_1 or A_2, would you select to obtain the better instrument? Give reasons, including relevant calculations, for your answer.■

Q 2.11 Self-assessment question
The diagram (figure 2.6) shows a moving-coil galvanometer, full-scale deflection 5.0 mA and resistance 10 Ω, which has been converted into a dual-range ammeter by the addition of shunts. Calculate the values of the resistances.■

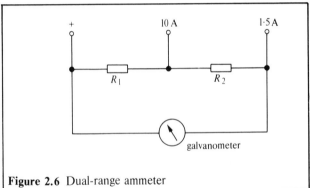

Figure 2.6 Dual-range ammeter

Q **2.12 Study question**
The circuit diagram (figure 2.7) shows the circuit of an ohmmeter. Explain qualitatively how it can be used to measure an unknown resistance. ∎

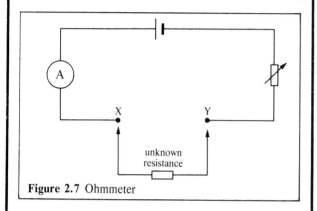

Figure 2.7 Ohmmeter

Q **2.13 Study question**
Design a multimeter for your own use which you could construct on the basis of a 50 μA, 75 Ω movement. Decide which ranges of current, p.d. and resistance you need, and work out suitable resistors and switching arrangements. For some ranges you may have to use resistors which dissipate a significant power (1 W or more): check this. If possible, construct your meter. ∎

2.2 The cathode ray oscilloscope

The cathode ray oscilloscope, or c.r.o., (figure 2.8) is one of the most versatile instruments that has been developed. It is used in the laboratory for the measurement of potential differences, and for displaying waveforms. A radar system uses a cathode ray tube to provide a map, a television picture is obtained on a cathode ray tube screen. Oscilloscopes are also used in hospitals in diagnosing heart disease or brain disorders, and monitoring patients' progress. These are only a few of many possible examples of its use.

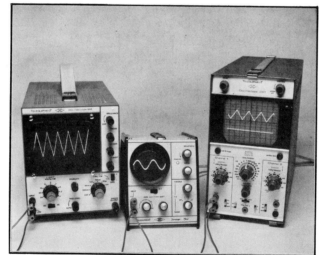

Figure 2.8

The cathode ray tube

The cathode ray tube, or c.r.t., (figure 2.9) consists of three basic parts.
(a) An *electron gun* which produces a beam of electrons focused on to the screen.
(b) A *deflecting system* which consists of two pairs of parallel plates arranged as shown in the figure.
(c) A *display system* consisting of a screen which is coated with a fluorescent material such as zinc sulphide.

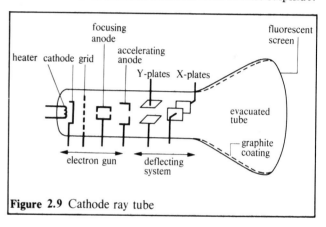

Figure 2.9 Cathode ray tube

Q **2.14 Study question**
Make brief notes, with diagrams, on the construction of the cathode ray tube. You should explain qualitatively:
(a) how the electrons are produced and accelerated;
(b) how the intensity of the beam, and hence the brightness of the spot, can be controlled;
(c) how the beam can be focused;
(d) how the beam can be deflected in vertical and horizontal directions;
(e) how the movement of the beam is displayed on the screen. ∎

The diagram, figure 2.10, shows the path taken by the electron beam when a p.d. is applied across the Y-plates of a c.r.t. It can be shown, by considering the force exerted on the electrons by the electric field between the plates, that the path is a parabola and that the deflection of the spot on the screen is proportional to the deflecting voltage, V. (This is considered in detail in the unit *Forces and fields*.)

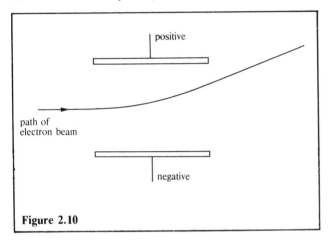

Figure 2.10

Q **2.15 Self-assessment question**
Sketch a diagram to show the path that would be taken if the p.d. across the Y-plates in figure 2.10 was reversed.■

Q **2.16 Self-assessment question**
(a) What meaning would you give to the 'sensitivity' of a c.r.t.?
(b) What is meant by the statement that the sensitivity of a certain c.r.t. for vertical deflection is 2 mm V^{-1}? Which of the following positions of the Y-gain switch, 50 V cm^{-1}, 5 V cm^{-1} or 0.5 V cm^{-1}, is the most sensitive? Give a reason for your answer.
(c) If an alternating p.d. of frequency 50 Hz is applied to the Y-plates of a c.r.t., what would you expect to observe on the screen? Give a reason for your answer.■

The time base
In order to find how a potential difference varies with time, we connect this varying p.d. to the Y-plates and connect the X-plates to the time base. The time base circuit produces a 'saw-tooth voltage' (figure 2.11), i.e. a potential difference which increases linearly with time and then rapidly decreases again. Using this time base, the X-deflection is proportional to time and the c.r.o. can draw graphs showing how the potential difference varies with time.

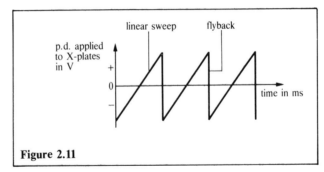

Figure 2.11

E **Experiment EP 4**
The cathode ray oscilloscope
The aim of this experiment is to use an oscilloscope to measure potential differences and time intervals, and to display waveforms.

Using the cathode ray oscilloscope
At first sight, a cathode ray oscilloscope may appear to be a very complicated piece of apparatus, but as you become familiar with the controls and their functions you will discover how useful it is as a tool in the laboratory. However, to use any complex tool properly it is essential to learn how it works, and what it can do. Figure 2.12 shows the controls of a typical c.r.o., and describes their functions.

There are three main uses for the c.r.o. in laboratory work.
1 *Measuring voltages*. This is the primary or basic use of the oscilloscope. The direct (or alternating) potential difference which is to be measured is connected across the Y-plates, with the time base switched off, so that with an alternating p.d. a vertical line is produced on the screen, from which the 'peak-to-peak' potential difference can be found. For a direct p.d., the actual shift of the spot is measured. In practice, it is often convenient to switch the time base on (preferably on a fast setting) to give a horizontal line. This may be easier for measurement and prevents the spot remaining stationary on the screen, which can harm the screen.

2 *Plotting waveforms*. The oscillating p.d. is applied to the Y-plates and the X-plates are connected to the time base. A suitable setting for the time base must be selected to give a useful trace.

3 *Measuring time intervals*. This is possible if the c.r.o. has a calibrated time base. The speed at which the trace goes across the screen is controlled by the time base circuit. If, for example, the time base is set at 100 ms cm^{-1}, this means that the spot travels 1 cm in 100 millisecond or 1/10 second.

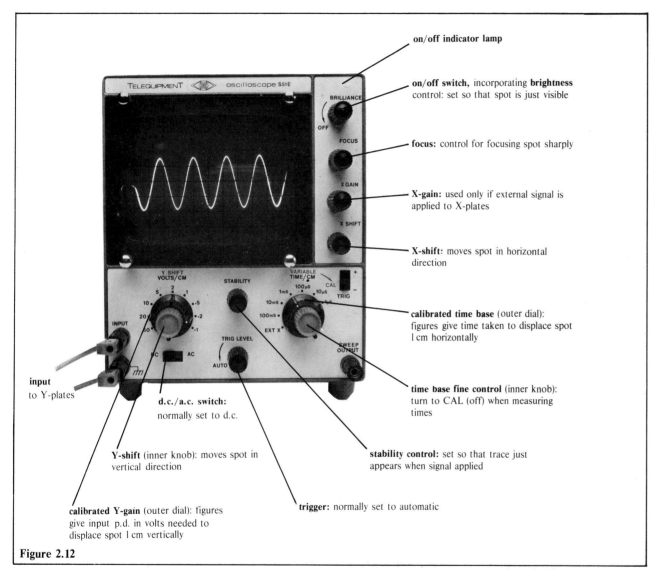

on/off indicator lamp

on/off switch, incorporating **brightness** control: set so that spot is just visible

focus: control for focusing spot sharply

X-gain: used only if external signal is applied to X-plates

X-shift: moves spot in horizontal direction

calibrated time base (outer dial): figures give time taken to displace spot 1 cm horizontally

time base fine control (inner knob): turn to CAL (off) when measuring times

stability control: set so that trace just appears when signal applied

trigger: normally set to automatic

input to Y-plates

d.c./a.c. switch: normally set to d.c.

Y-shift (inner knob): moves spot in vertical direction

calibrated Y-gain (outer dial): figures give input p.d. in volts needed to displace spot 1 cm vertically

Figure 2.12

Background reading
A book which will give you some idea of the usefulness of the c.r.o., and show you how to operate it, is *Using the cathode ray oscilloscope* by E. Howard.

Q 2.17 Study question
What are the main advantages of the c.r.o. as a voltmeter, as compared with a moving coil voltmeter?∎

Q 2.18 Self-assessment question
(a) The gain control of an oscilloscope is set on 2.0 V cm^{-1}. What is the peak value of an alternating p.d. which produces a vertical line-trace 50 mm long when the time base is switched off?
(b) When an alternating current is passed through a 200 Ω resistor whose ends are connected to the Y-plates of a c.r.o., the trace on the screen is a vertical line 60 mm long. When a steady p.d. is applied to these plates it gives a displacement of 0.20 mm V^{-1}. Calculate the peak value of the alternating current.∎

Q 2.19 Self-assessment question
What is the frequency of an alternating p.d. which, when applied to the Y-plates of a c.r.o., produces 20 complete cycles on a 10 cm length of screen when the time base is set at 10 ms cm^{-1}?∎

Q 2.20 Self-assessment question
An alternating p.d. of frequency 50 Hz is connected across the Y-plates of a c.r.o. Sketch and explain the forms of the traces on the screen when linear time bases of the following frequencies are connected across the X-plates:
(a) 10 Hz,
(b) 100 Hz.∎

2.3 The potentiometer

The potential divider

In an electric circuit it is often necessary to divide a p.d. into two or more parts and this can be achieved by connecting two or more resistors in series across the supply.

Q 2.21 Self-assessment question
A battery of e.m.f. 12.0 V and internal resistance 0.50 Ω is connected to two resistors R_1 and R_2, of resistances 3.5 Ω and 2.0 Ω respectively, as shown in figure 2.13.
(a) Calculate the p.d. across the terminals of the battery and across the resistor R_1.
(b) Why is the p.d. across the terminals of the battery less than the e.m.f. of the battery?■

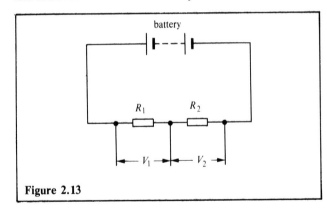

Figure 2.13

An important application of a two-resistor potential divider is to provide the correct potential difference to a transistor between, e.g., the base and emitter (the transistor will be introduced in chapter 4).

Q 2.22 Self-assessment question
The diagram, figure 2.14, shows how two resistors are used to maintain the base of a transistor at a positive potential relative to the emitter. Calculate the p.d. across the 1 kΩ resistor. Assume that negligible current passes into the transistor at the junction X.■

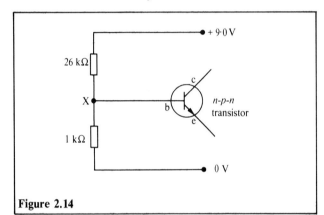

Figure 2.14

By choosing suitable values for R_1 and R_2 in figure 2.13 we can obtain a range of potential differences across the resistors. If the two fixed resistors are replaced by a single fixed resistor with a variable contact, then it is possible to have a continuously variable voltage supply. When a variable resistor is used in this way, as in figure 2.15, it is referred to as a potential divider or as a potentiometer.
Note: You should not confuse the jargon term 'potentiometer', applied to a specific use of a variable resistor, with the technical term potentiometer used for a precision measuring instrument.

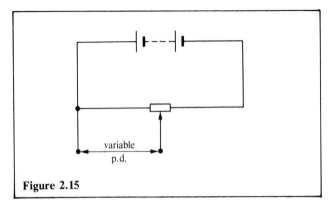

Figure 2.15

EXTENSION

Q 2.23 Study question
Look in your text book at a drawing or photograph of a rotary potentiometer, as used for the volume control of a radio or television. Find out the difference between wire-wound and carbon-track potentiometers, and between 'linear' and 'log' potentiometers. A supplier's catalogue may be useful.■

The slide-wire potentiometer

This consists of a length of uniform resistance wire AB connected across a battery (driver cell), as shown in figure 2.16. A movable contact J can be placed at any position along the wire. In this way a potential difference between A and J can be obtained which ranges from zero to the maximum p.d. provided by the battery. Most slide-wire potentiometers used in schools and colleges are exactly a metre long, but longer wires are sometimes used. In this case they are usually arranged in one-metre sections.

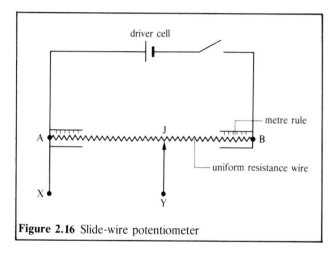

Figure 2.16 Slide-wire potentiometer

E Experiment EP 5
The potentiometer

In this experiment you will find out how the p.d. along a uniform wire depends upon the length of the wire and consider the principles of the potentiometer circuit.

Theory of the slide-wire potentiometer

The p.d. across the wire of a slide-wire potentiometer is proportional to the length of the wire. It is possible to derive this relationship theoretically.

Suppose that the wire has a resistance per unit length of σ and that a steady current I passes through it, as in figure 2.17a. Consider a point J on the wire. The p.d. across AJ is $I\sigma l$. If I and σ are constant, then the p.d. is proportional to the length along the wire.

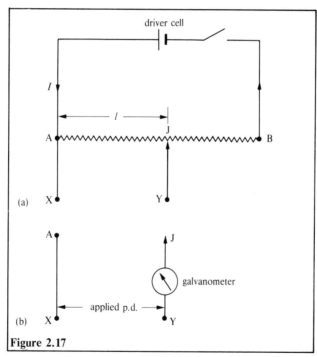

Figure 2.17

Q 2.24 Self-assessment question
(a) Why is it important to use a uniform wire?
(b) Why is it important in a potentiometer experiment that the driver cell maintains a steady current along the potentiometer wire? Why is a lead–acid accumulator a good choice? Why would a dry cell be a poor choice?■

The p.d. V which is to be compared is applied between the points X and Y (figure 2.17a), and the positive and negative terminals are connected to X and Y respectively. A galvanometer is placed as shown in figure 2.17b.

The position of the point J is adjusted so that the reading on the galvanometer is zero. This occurs when the two potential differences (the p.d. along the wire and the applied p.d.) balance. The applied p.d. is then equal to the p.d. across the length l of the wire, so

$$V = I\sigma l.$$

This is the basic potentiometer relationship.

Q 2.25 Self-assessment question
(a) Why is the relation $V = I\sigma l$ *not* true when a current passes through the galvanometer?
(b) Would connecting the galvanometer between A and X instead of J and Y make any difference to the instrument?■

Q **2.26 Self-assessment question**

In the potentiometer circuit shown in figure 2.18, D is a driver cell which has a terminal p.d. of 2.0 V, AB is a two-metre length of uniform wire of resistance 4.0 Ω and C is a cell of e.m.f. 1.5 V. The position of the sliding contact is adjusted until the reading on the galvanometer is zero.

(a) What is the balance length?

(b) A 1.0 Ω resistor is placed in series with the driver cell and the potentiometer. Explain why the cell C is no longer balanced. What is the new p.d. across the potentiometer wire (assume that the internal resistance of D is negligible)? What is the new balance length?■

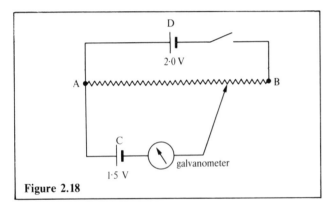

Figure 2.18

Q **2.27 Study question**

A potentiometer does the same job as a moving-coil voltmeter. What are the advantages and disadvantages of each?■

2.4 Applications of the potentiometer

A potentiometer can be used to compare potential differences. It can also be used to compare currents and resistances. For *measuring* these quantities the potentiometer must be calibrated using a standard e.m.f. You will now consider how the potentiometer can be used to measure:

(a) electromotive force and internal resistance of a source of electrical energy, for example, a battery;

(b) the current passing through a given resistor;

(c) the resistance of a given resistor;

(d) a small p.d., for example, the e.m.f. of a thermocouple.

For each of these measurements, you should be able to set up the circuit, draw the circuit diagram, explain how the measurements are taken and explain how you would use your experimental results to calculate the required physical quantity.

Measurement of e.m.f. and p.d.

Q **2.28 Self-assessment question**

To compare the e.m.f.s of two cells, E_1 and E_2, they were connected in turn between X and Y as shown in figure 2.19 and the corresponding balance lengths l_1 and l_2 obtained.

(a) Show that

$$\frac{E_1}{E_2} = \frac{l_1}{l_2}$$

(b) Explain why it is more appropriate to compare E_1 with E_2 than with the e.m.f. of the driver cell. If E_1 is unknown, what type of cell would be chosen for E_2?

(c) What is the advantage of making the balance-point near to B?

(d) Why should you take several readings, if possible?

(e) What size of resistance is appropriate for protecting the galvanometer with (i) a series resistor, (ii) a shunt?■

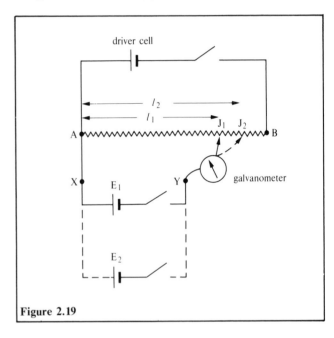

Figure 2.19

Q **2.29 Study question**

Explain, with the aid of a circuit diagram, how you would use a potentiometer to calibrate a voltmeter.■

Internal resistance of a cell

The potentiometer provides an accurate method of measuring the internal resistance of a cell. The circuit is shown in figure 2.20. The balance length is l_0 when the switch is open and l when the switch is closed.

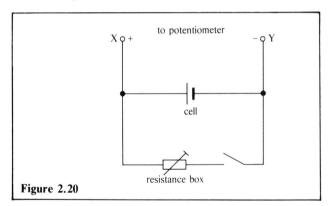

Figure 2.20

Q 2.31 Self-assessment question
(a) Show that the relation between the e.m.f. E of a cell of internal resistance r and the p.d. V across its terminals when they are connected by a resistance R is

$$\frac{E}{V} = 1 + \frac{r}{R}$$

(b) Explain why

$$\frac{E}{V} = \frac{l_0}{l}$$

(c) In an experiment to determine the internal resistance of a cell (which is assumed to be constant), a student obtained a series of values for the balance length l and the corresponding resistance R. He then plotted a graph of l_0/l (y-axis) against $1/R$ (x-axis). Sketch the shape of his graph and explain how a value for the internal resistance can be found from the graph. (Hint: From (a) and (b),

$$\frac{l_0}{l} = \frac{r}{R} + 1.$$

Compare this with the equation for a straight line, $y = mx + c$.)

(d) Another student plotted a graph of $1/R$ (y-axis) against $1/l$ (x-axis). Sketch the shape of this graph and explain how the value of the internal resistance can be found from the graph.∎

E Experiment EP 6
Internal resistance of a cell using a potentiometer
A source of electrical energy has an *internal resistance*, and when it delivers a current I, the p.d. across its terminals falls by Ir, where r is the internal resistance of the source. In this experiment you will gain experience in using a potentiometer circuit and measure the internal resistance of a cell.

Q 2.32 Self-assessment question
A cell on open circuit is balanced by 150 cm of potentiometer wire. When the cell is passing a current through a resistance of 5.00 Ω, the balance length across the terminals of the cell is reduced to 125 cm. Calculate the internal resistance of the cell.∎

Measurement of current

The potentiometer circuit can be adapted for the measurement of current. The potentiometer terminals X and Y are connected across a known resistance as shown in figure 2.21. Suppose a current I passes through the known resistance R. The potentiometer measures the p.d. V across the resistance. Thus $I = V/R$.

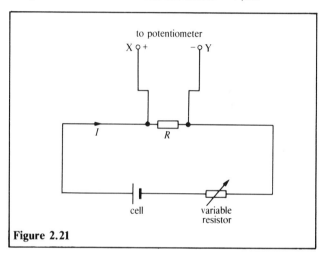

Figure 2.21

Q 2.33 Study question
Explain, with the aid of a circuit diagram, how you would use a potentiometer to calibrate an ammeter. Suggest the range of currents it is appropriate to measure in this way, giving your reasons. Explain why a resistor which is used in a potentiometer experiment often has four terminals (two current and two potential terminals).∎

Comparison of resistances

The potentiometer provides an accurate method of comparing two resistances. The circuit is shown in figure 2.22. The potentiometer terminals X and Y are connected in turn across R_1 and R_2 and the corresponding balance lengths l_1 and l_2 are found.

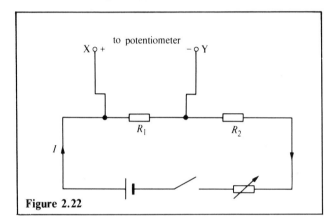

Figure 2.22

Q **2.34 Self-assessment question**
If a current I is passed through the two resistors R_1 and R_2, connected in series, show that

$$\frac{R_1}{R_2} = \frac{l_1}{l_2}$$

where l_1 and l_2 are the balance lengths.∎

Q **2.35 Self-assessment question**
(a) In an experiment to determine the resistivity of copper, a length of copper wire of resistance R_1 is connected in series with a standard resistor R_2 of value 0.020 Ω, an accumulator of e.m.f. 2.0 V and a resistor R of about 20 Ω. The p.d.s across R_1 and R_2 are compared

by means of a potentiometer circuit, which consists of a uniform wire of resistance 40 Ω, a resistor S in series with the wire, and a driver cell of e.m.f. 2.0 V and negligible internal resistance. Explain why the resistor R is included in the circuit and estimate a value for the resistance S.∎

E **Experiment EP 7**
Measuring resistance with a potentiometer
In this experiment you will determine the resistance of a resistor by comparing the p.d.s across an unknown and a known resistor when the same current passes through them.

Thermoelectric effect

When two different metals or alloys are joined together to form a complete circuit, and the two junctions maintained at different temperatures, a current passes through the circuit indicating the existence of an e.m.f. This effect was discovered in 1826 and is referred to as the *Seebeck effect*. The arrangement is known as a *thermocouple*.

This effect, in the case of metals, is on too small a scale to provide a useful source of energy. However, in the past twenty years, thermocouples consisting of semiconducting materials have been found to be effective as energy sources.

Because the thermoelectric e.m.f. is dependent upon temperature differences, the thermocouple is used as a means of detecting and measuring the power of radiation. It can also be used as a means of measuring temperature (this will be considered in the unit *Thermal properties*).

Measurement of a small p.d.

Q **2.36 Development question***
In a potentiometer experiment to measure a thermoelectric e.m.f., the driver cell has an e.m.f. E and negligible internal resistance, the series resistance is R and the resistance of the potentiometer wire of length L is S.
(a) Write down an expression for the current I passing through the potentiometer wire.
(b) What is the p.d. across the whole length of the potentiometer wire?
(c) If the thermoelectric e.m.f. V gives a balance length l, show that

$$V = \frac{ES}{(R + S)} \times \frac{l}{L}.∎$$

Q **2.37 Self-assessment question**
A resistance of 1000 Ω was placed in series with a 5 m length of potentiometer wire of resistance 5.0 Ω m⁻¹. A balance length was obtained when a standard cell of e.m.f. 1.018 V was connected across the 1000 Ω resistor and 480 cm of potentiometer wire. When the thermocouple was connected, a balance was obtained across 122.5 cm of potentiometer wire. Calculate the e.m.f. of the thermocouple from this experimental data.∎

E **Experiment EP 8**
Thermoelectric e.m.f. and temperature
A thermoelectric e.m.f. can be measured by a potentiometer. However, because the e.m.f. of the thermocouple is small, the potentiometer circuit has to be modified so that the p.d. across the potentiometer wire is of the order of millivolts. This is achieved by placing a high resistance R in series with the potentiometer wire.

Comprehension exercise

(Adapted from London A level, Paper 3, 1976.)
This type of examination question is designed to test your ability to plot graphs from given experimental data and to make use of the graphs to determine appropriate physical constants.

Read the following account of an experimental investigation and then answer the questions at the end.

Figure 2.23 shows part of a circuit, consisting of a piece of iron wire and two pieces of copper wire, joined at the junctions A and B. During an experiment the temperature of junction A was maintained at 0 °C, while the temperature of junction B was raised to various temperatures θ. A potentiometer was used to measure the potential difference V between X and Y, for a series of values of θ, with the following results.

$\theta/°C$	V/mV
240	1.593
250	1.608
260	1.616
270	1.623
280	1.625
290	1.622
300	1.614
310	1.603
320	1.588

The equation representing the way in which V varies with temperature may be written

$$V = a\theta \ (2\theta_m - \theta) \qquad (1)$$

where θ_m is the temperature at which V has its maximum value.

The slope s of the graph of V against θ at any temperature may be written

$$s = 2a \ (\theta_m - \theta) \qquad (2)$$

1 Plot a graph with V as ordinate (y-axis) and θ as abscissa (x-axis). Record θ_m, the temperature at which V has its maximum value.

2 (a) Draw a tangent to your curve, at a temperature θ_1, less than θ_m, and determine its slope s_1.
(b) Draw a second tangent at a temperature θ_2, greater than θ_m, and determine its slope s_2.

Using equation (2), your value of θ_m obtained in question 1 and your values of s_1 and s_2, calculate a mean value for a.

3 Plot a graph with V/θ as ordinate and θ as abscissa. Determine the slope β of the line. From equation (1) and your value of β, obtain a further value for a.

4 Discuss the relative accuracy of the values of a obtained in question 2 and question 3.

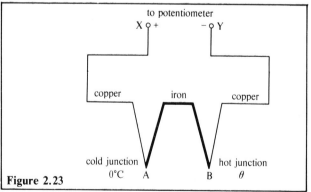

to potentiometer
X o +   – o Y

copper   iron   copper

cold junction   hot junction
0°C   A   B θ

Figure 2.23

SYLLABUS EXTENSION

2.5 The Wheatstone bridge

This section deals with the principle of the Wheatstone bridge circuit, and considers its use as a method of determining resistance.

Principle of Wheatstone bridge circuit

The network of resistors shown in figure 2.24 is arranged in what is known as the Wheatstone bridge circuit. If the resistances P, Q, R and S are adjusted so that no current passes through the galvanometer, then the bridge is said to be *balanced*.

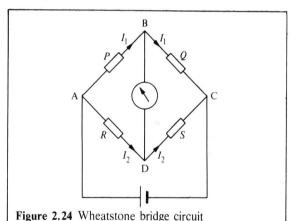

Figure 2.24 Wheatstone bridge circuit

Q **2.38 Development question***
When the bridge is balanced (figure 2.24), no current passes through the galvanometer. This means that the potential difference across BD is zero; that is, B and D are at the same potential.

(a) Write down expressions for the p.d. across AB and the p.d. across AD.

(b) Explain why these p.d.s are equal, that is why $I_1 P = I_2 R$.

(c) Similarly show that $I_1 Q = I_2 S$.

(d) Hence show that

$$\frac{P}{Q} = \frac{R}{S}$$

(e) Show that the same condition holds if the position of the cell and galvanometer are interchanged.■

An unknown resistance P can therefore be found by knowing the value of Q, and the ratio R/S.

Q **2.39 Self-assessment question**
Four resistors AB, BC, CD and DA of resistances 4.0 Ω, 8.0 Ω, 4.0 Ω and 8.0 Ω respectively are connected so as to form a closed network. The positive terminal of a battery of e.m.f. 6.0 V and negligible resistance is connected to A and the negative terminal to C.

(a) Calculate the p.d. between A and B and the p.d. between A and D. Explain why a current would pass through a galvanometer connected between B and D.

(b) Calculate the value of the additional resistance which must be connected between A and D so that no current passes through the galvanometer.■

The metre bridge

A practical application of the Wheatstone bridge circuit is the metre bridge, in which the resistors R and S are parts of a uniform resistance wire. The ratio R/S can be found from the ratio of the balance lengths l_1 and l_2 (figure 2.25).

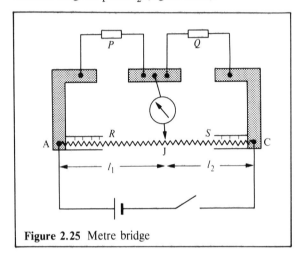

Figure 2.25 Metre bridge

Q **2.40 Self-assessment question**
Show that for a metre bridge we can write

$$\frac{R}{S} = \frac{l_1}{l_2}$$

where l_1 and l_2 are the lengths of resistance wire when the bridge is balanced.■

E **Experiment EP 9**
Measuring resistance with a metre bridge
In this experiment you will use a metre bridge to determine the value of an unknown resistance.

Q **2.41 Self-assessment question**
Explain why the Wheatstone bridge circuit is unsuitable for the comparison of:

(a) two low resistances (of the order 10^{-1} Ω);

(b) two high resistances (of the order 10^9 Ω).

Q **2.42 Study question**
(a) Explain why a metre bridge is most accurate when the balance point is near the middle of the bridge wire.

(b) What errors are minimised by interchanging the known and unknown resistances?

(c) What errors are minimised by reversing the direction of the current?

(d) What type of wire should be used for connecting the known and unknown resistances to the bridge terminals? Give a reason for your answer.■

Q **2.43 Self-assessment question**
A Wheatstone bridge contains a standard resistance of 5.00 Ω, an unknown resistance and a metre length of uniform resistance wire. A balance point is found 35.0 cm along the wire, measured from the end to which the standard resistance is connected. Calculate the value of the unknown resistance.■

E **Experiment EP 10** (optional)
Temperature coefficient of resistance
In this experiment you will use a metre bridge to measure the resistance of a coil of copper wire over a range of temperatures, and from your results plot a graph from which the temperature coefficient of resistance of copper can be calculated.

Questions on objectives

1 The maximum current that can be passed through the coil of a moving coil galvanometer is 2.0 mA. The galvanometer has a resistance of 50 Ω. Explain how it can be adapted to measure:

(a) the current in an electric cable carrying up to 20 A;
(b) the p.d. between two points, which may have a maximum value of 150 V.

(objectives 2 and 7)

2 The Y-plates of a c.r.o. are connected to a sinusoidal alternating p.d. of frequency 200 Hz and a peak voltage of 6 V. Draw the trace you would expect to observe on the screen in each of the following cases if the Y-gain control is set at 4 V cm⁻¹.

(a) The time base is switched off and no signal is applied to the X-plates.
(b) The time base is set at 5 ms cm⁻¹.

(objective 3)

3 The trace shown in figure 2.26 is that of an alternating p.d. with the time base set at 5 ms cm⁻¹. Calculate the frequency of the supply.

(objective 3)

4 For measuring the e.m.f. of a cell, what advantage does a potentiometer method possess over a moving-coil voltmeter?

(objectives 2 and 4)

5 When using a potentiometer, what is the advantage of obtaining a balance point near the end of the wire?

(objective 4)

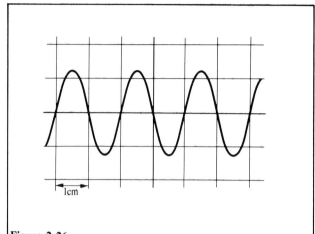

Figure 2.26

6 What action would you take if, when using a potentiometer to compare the e.m.f.s of two cells, you observed the following?
The deflection of the galvanometer needle
(a) varies steadily as the sliding contact is moved along the potentiometer wire, but is always in the same direction;
(b) has the same value (not zero) for all positions of the sliding contact.
(*Note:* this question does not assume a correct potentiometer circuit.)

(objective 5)

7 In a potentiometer experiment to measure current, a balance length of 90.0 cm was obtained when the current flowed through a standard resistance of 1.500 Ω. A standard cell of e.m.f. 1.018 V was balanced by the potential drop along a 120.0 cm length of the potentiometer wire.

Draw a labelled circuit diagram and calculate, from first principles, the current through the resistor. State clearly the assumptions that you make in your calculations.

(objectives 5, 6 and 7)

8 A potentiometer wire is used in an experiment to determine the internal resistance of a cell. The e.m.f. of the cell is balanced by the fall in potential along 96.0 cm of wire. When a resistance of 10.00 Ω is connected across the cell, the balance length is found to be 80.0 cm. Draw a labelled circuit diagram, and calculate from first principles the internal resistance of the cell.

(objectives 5, 6 and 7)

9 EXTENSION
(a) Explain the theory of the Wheatstone bridge method of comparing resistances.
(b) What advantage is gained by arranging for the balance point to be near the centre of a metre bridge wire?
(c) Why is a Wheatstone bridge unsuitable for comparing very low resistances?

(objective 8)

10 EXTENSION
A metre bridge is balanced with a piece of aluminium wire of resistance 7.30 Ω in the left-hand gap, the sliding contact (jockey) being 42.6 cm from the left-hand end of the bridge wire and the temperature 17 °C. If the temperature of the aluminium wire is raised to 57 °C, how may the balance be restored
(a) by adjusting the sliding contact;
(b) by keeping the contact at 42.6 cm and connecting a resistor in parallel with the aluminium wire.
(temperature coefficient of resistance of aluminium = 3.8 × 10⁻³ K⁻¹).

(objective 10)

Conduction in liquids and gases

Aim
SYLLABUS EXTENSION
In this chapter you will learn about the way in which liquids (electrolytes) and gases conduct electricity, and how this provides evidence about the nature of electric charge.

Chapter 3

Objectives

When you have completed the work in this chapter you should be able to:

1   Use the following scientific terms correctly: anode, cathode, electrode, electrolyte, electrolysis, primary cell, secondary cell, saturation current, avalanche current.

2   Define and use the following scientific term: Faraday constant.

3   State the relationship between the mass of substance deposited or liberated during electrolysis and the electric charge.

4   Describe and explain the conduction of electricity through an electrolyte in terms of positive and negative ions.

5   Describe and explain the chemical changes that occur in electrolysis, with particular reference to the electrolysis of copper sulphate solution using (a) copper electrodes, and (b) carbon or platinum electrodes.

6   Sketch and explain graphs to show the variation of current with applied potential difference for an electrolyte.

7   Show how the charge on an ion can be related to the Faraday constant and the Avogadro constant.

8   Solve problems involving a knowledge of the Faraday constant.

9   Describe and explain the mechanism of conduction of electricity through a gas.

10 Sketch and explain a graph to show the variation of current with potential difference for a gas.

11 EXTENSION
Describe the construction and explain the action of a primary cell, a secondary cell and a fuel cell, and give an outline of their applications.

12 EXTENSION
Describe the conduction of electricity by gases at low pressure.

Experiments in chapter 3

EP 11 Movement of ions in an electric field
(½ hour)
EP 12 Current–p.d. relationship for electrolytes
(optional) (1 hour)
EP 13 Current–p.d. relationship for a gas (optional)
(½ hour)

References

Bennet	Chapters 3 and 13
Brown	Chapters 5 and 21
Duncan MM	Chapter 3
Duncan FWA	Chapter 10
Nelkon	Chapters 35 and 41

3.1 Conduction in liquids

A liquid in which a chemical change takes place when an electric current passes through is called an *electrolyte*: the process is called *electrolysis*.

Ionisation in a liquid

A solid such as sodium chloride consists of a regular structure of sodium ions and chloride ions which are held together (or bonded) by electric forces. This type of bonding is called ionic bonding (it is considered in the unit *Structure of matter*). When such substances are dissolved in water the net forces holding the ions together are weakened and the positive and negative ions can separate and move about at random in the solution.

Q **3.1 Study question***
A potential difference is applied across two plates (or electrodes) which are placed into an electrolyte as shown in figure 3.1.

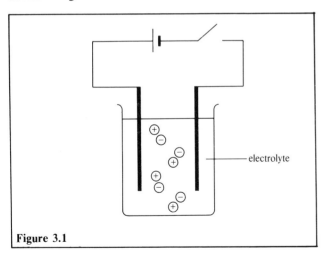

Figure 3.1

(a) Copy this diagram and label the anode and the cathode.
(b) An electric field is created between the electrodes which causes a force to be exerted on the ions. Explain what happens to the ions.■

Faraday did a great deal of work to provide an understanding of the conduction of an electric current in a liquid. By 1834 he had formulated his laws of electrolysis and explained conduction in an electrolyte in terms of the movement of ions. It was Arrhenius, however, who in 1887 explained the formation of positive and negative ions and their movement under the influence of an electric field. In 1857 Clausius had put forward the theory that ions carried particular charges whose sizes he was able to calculate, but it was not until the late 19th century that it was realised that the sizes of these charges were multiples of the charge on the electron.

Although it is not possible to observe directly the movement of ions, it is possible to demonstrate that movement is taking place.

E **Experiment EP 11**
Movement of ions in an electric field
In this experiment you will investigate the mobility of ions. You will see that they move under the influence of an electric field, certain ions moving in one direction while others move in the opposite direction.

Chemical changes

Conduction in an electrolyte takes place only by the movement of ions. The electrodes must normally be made of metal (or carbon) and in such a material the conduction is due to the movement of free electrons. Thus the mechanism of conduction must change at the electrodes. This can happen in one of two ways:
(a) ions are formed from the material of the electrode and pass into solution,
(b) ions are discharged, i.e. give up their excess electrons if they are negative or accept electrons if they are positive.

The chemical changes that occur in electrolysis are due to what happens at the electrodes. This can be illustrated by considering the electrolysis of copper sulphate solution. In solution copper sulphate consists of copper Cu^{2+} ions and sulphate SO_4^{2-} ions. The water itself provides small quantities of hydrogen H^+ ions and hydroxyl OH^- ions. (The symbol Cu^{2+} represents a doubly-ionised copper atom – a copper atom which has lost 2 electrons. Sometimes the same symbol is used to represent *a mole* of such ions.) Both sorts of positive ions travel towards the cathode but the Cu^{2+} ions are discharged in preference to the H^+ ions.

We can write the following equation to represent what happens at the cathode:
$$Cu^{2+}(aq) + 2e^- \rightarrow Cu(s).$$
In this equation the physical states of substances are indicated: (aq) means dissolved in water, (s) means solid state. Other symbols used to indicate physical state are (l) for liquid state and (g) for gaseous state.

The negative ions travel towards the anode. What happens there depends upon the type of electrode. If the electrodes are copper, experiments show that the gain in mass at the cathode is equal to the loss of mass at the anode, so the anode reaction must be
$$Cu(s) \rightarrow Cu^{2+}(aq) + 2e^-.$$
The net effect is that copper is transferred from the anode to the cathode. This is the basis of the manufacture of pure copper from impure copper.

Q **3.2 Self-assessment question**
Explain in words the meaning of the equations for the cathode and anode reactions. ∎

If the electrodes are carbon, copper is again deposited at the cathode but oxygen is liberated at the anode. This can come only from the water, since there is no evidence of the formation of sulphur compounds which would be expected if the sulphate ions were discharged. This process can be represented by
$$2OH^-(aq) \rightarrow H_2O(l) + O + 2e^-,$$
which would be followed by
$$O + O \rightarrow O_2(g).$$

Q **3.3 Study question**
Write a brief summary of how electricity is conducted through a metal, and how it is conducted through a solution of copper sulphate. ∎

Faraday's first law
Electrolysis was investigated quantitatively by Faraday who found how the mass of substance deposited or liberated during electrolysis depended upon the electric charge.

Q **3.4 Study question**
(a) Write out a statement of Faraday's first law of electrolysis.
(b) Outline an experiment with a copper voltameter to verify this law. State what measurements you would take and the precautions you would take in order to obtain accurate results.
(c) Show how you would use the results of your experiment to determine the specific charge on the copper ion. ∎

Q **3.5 Self-assessment question**
In an electroplating experiment, you may find that the deposit on the electrode flakes off very easily. Why is this, and how would you prevent it so that you could achieve a good electroplated surface? ∎

Q **3.6 Self-assessment question**
The word electrolysis comes from the roots 'electro' and 'lysis'. 'Lysis' means decomposition. Discuss why electrolysis is a good word to describe the operation of conduction in a liquid. ∎

Q **3.7 Self-assessment question**
Copper and aluminium are refined using electrolytic processes. In fact, it was Hall's discovery of the electrolytic extraction process that enabled aluminium to be processed economically and in large quantities. Both copper and aluminium exist naturally in their oxide forms and it is very difficult to separate the metal.
(a) Calculate the charge needed to produce one kilogram of aluminium. The mass of aluminium deposited by the passage of 1 C is 9.3×10^{-8} kg.
(b) If the p.d. applied to a typical industrial cell is 5 V, what is the energy required to produce one kilogram of aluminium?
(c) If a factory produces 5×10^3 kg of aluminium per day, what is the energy consumption per day?
(d) If the production process is 60% efficient, what is the total energy consumption of the plant in one day?
(e) Calculate the cost of the electricity which is required to produce the aluminium if electricity costs 2.5p per kilowatt hour. ∎

3.2 Faraday constant
Faraday's first law states that the mass of substance liberated in electrolysis is proportional to the electric charge that liberated it. If we consider the electrolysis of copper sulphate,
$$Cu^{2+}(aq) + 2e^- \rightarrow Cu(s).$$
Positive ions move to the cathode and gain electrons. One atom of copper is deposited by the passage of two electrons.

The mole
In discussion of electrolysis, it is convenient to consider a quantity of charges or particles known as a *mole*. This unit is used to compare equal numbers of atoms, molecules, ions, electrons, etc., and is defined as follows:

The mole is the amount of substance which contains as many elementary particles, or specified groups of particles, as there are atoms in 0.012 kilogram of carbon 12.

In other words, a mole is a bundle of 6.0×10^{23} particles, or specified groups of particles. This number is known as the Avogadro constant, and is stated here to two significant figures. (The mole and the Avogadro constant are dealt with more fully in the unit *Structure of matter*. For this unit the idea of 'bundles of particles' is adequate.)

In terms of moles, the equation for the electrolysis of copper sulphate shows that one mole of copper atoms is deposited by the passage of two moles of electrons.

For one mole of atoms of a substance to be deposited or liberated at an electrode, one, two, or more, moles of charge are required, depending upon whether the ion of that substance has lost or gained one, two, or more, electrons. The charge per mole of electrons (or singly charged ions) is called the Faraday constant F. Its value is 9.6×10^4 C mol^{-1}, to two significant figures.

The mass of a mole of atoms is equal to the relative atomic mass in grams. For example, 1 mole of copper atoms has a mass of 63.5 g.

Worked example
What mass of copper is deposited at the cathode when a current of 0.20 A passes for 30 minutes?

The copper ion is Cu^{2+}, and the relative atomic mass of copper is 63.5. One mole of copper atoms is deposited by two moles of electrons. One mole of electrons has a charge of 9.6×10^4 C.
Therefore $2 \times 9.6 \times 10^4$ C are needed to deposit 63.5 g of copper.
Total charge flowing = $0.20 \times 30 \times 60$ C
$$= 360 \text{ C.}$$
360 C will deposit $\dfrac{63.5}{2 \times 9.6 \times 10^4} \times 360$ g of copper
$$= 0.12 \text{ g of copper.}$$

Q **3.8 Study question***
Write out a definition of the Faraday constant. ∎

Q **3.9 Self-assessment question**
(a) Calculate the mass of silver deposited at the cathode during electrolysis of silver nitrate solution when a current of 0.50 A passes for 45 minutes. (Relative atomic mass of silver = 108, the silver ion is Ag^+.)
(b) How long will it take to deposit 5.00 g of tin at a cathode if a current of 0.75 A is passed through the electrolyte? (Relative atomic mass of tin = 118.7, the tin ion is Sn^{2+}.) ∎

Charge on an electron
From a knowledge of the Faraday constant and the number of atoms in a mole of any substance (the Avogadro constant), it is possible to calculate the charge carried by a singly charged ion and hence the charge on the electron.

Q **3.10 Self-assessment question**
Use the following data to determine the charge carried by a singly charged ion:
Faraday constant = 9.6×10^4 C mol^{-1},
Avogadro constant = 6.0×10^{23} mol^{-1}. ∎

For a singly charged ion
$$F = N_A e$$
where e is the elementary charge and N_A is the Avogadro constant.

The expression $F = N_A e$ provides one of the most accurate ways of measuring e. F is found by electrolysis and N_A from X-ray crystallography measurements.

3.3 Current-potential difference relationships

E **Experiment EP 12 (optional)**
Current–p.d. relationship for electrolytes
The aim of this experiment is to investigate the relationship between applied p.d. and current for electrolytes.

Experimental investigation of the variation of current through an electrolyte with the applied p.d., to find out whether electrolytes obey Ohm's law, shows that different results are obtained with different electrolytes. The results of two such experiments are summarised below.

1 With copper sulphate solution and copper electrodes, the current is proportional to the applied p.d., as shown in figure 3.2.

2 With acidified water (a dilute solution of sulphuric acid) and platinum or carbon electrodes, conduction does not take place until the p.d. reaches a certain value, as shown in figure 3.3. The reason for this is that the voltameter acts like a cell, producing an e.m.f. in opposition to the applied p.d. This e.m.f. is due to polarisation, that is, the films of gas formed at the electrodes (oxygen at the anode and hydrogen at the cathode) when the circuit is first connected. This e.m.f. is often called a polarising or *back e.m.f.*

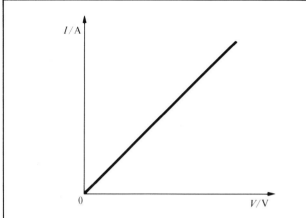

Figure 3.2 Current-p.d. relationship for copper sulphate solution with copper electrodes

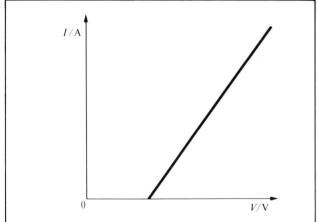

Figure 3.3 Current-p.d. relationship for acidified water with inert electrodes

EXTENSION

3.4 Electric cells

The chemical effects associated with electric currents were used as a source of electrical energy for many years before Faraday formulated his laws. By 1800, Volta (an Italian professor in Pavia) had reported to the Royal Society a device he called his 'crown of cups'. It was what we would now refer to as a bank of simple cells. In his work leading up to this, he worked out experimentally the 'voltaic series', upon which our modern electrochemical series is based. He also invented the 'voltaic pile' – a bank of several copper/zinc cells.

Many types of chemical cell have been developed since the time of Volta. They are all basically the same; different materials (usually metals) separated by an electrolyte, together with a means of preventing (or at least limiting) polarisation, that is, the decline in effectiveness of a cell during use.

Q **3.11 Study question**
Cells can be classified in two major groups – primary and secondary. Outline the main features of each type, bringing out both the similarities and differences between them.■

Q **3.12 Study question**
Polarisation has a limiting effect on the performance of a primary cell. Describe what causes polarisation and hence explain why it affects the cell's operation.■

Q **3.13 Self-assessment question**
(a) A battery of accumulators of e.m.f. 50 V and internal resistance 0.20 Ω is charged from a 100 V d.c. supply. What series resistance will be required if the charging current is to be 2.0 A?
(b) If electricity costs 2.5 pence per kilowatt hour, what will it cost to recharge the battery for 8 hours? What percentage of the energy supplied will be wasted as internal energy?■

Q **3.14 Study question**
For each of the applications labelled (a) to (e), state which of the cells, labelled 1 to 8, you would use. Give the reasons for your choice (you may choose more than one cell, if appropriate).

Applications
(a) door bell
(b) car battery
(c) calibration (e.g. of a potentiometer
(d) pacemaker (for people with weak hearts)
(e) electric car

Cells
1 Daniell cell
2 Leclanché cell
3 dry cell
4 Weston cell
5 fuel cell
6 lead–acid accumulator
7 nickel–iron accumulator
8 nickel–cadmium accumulator.■

Q **3.15 Study question**
Work is now being done to develop the 'fuel cell'. This is a type of primary cell in which fresh chemicals are continuously added. It has potential as a power supply for an electric car. Write an account of the development, operation and application of the fuel cell.■

3.5 Conduction in gases

The examination of the conduction of electricity through gases is dealt with only briefly in this section. It was the study of the conditions needed in gases to get charges to flow, and the way in which they did flow, that led to Thomson's discovery of the electron. This developed further our understanding of the atom. (Ideas of atomic structure are introduced in the unit *Structure of matter* and extended in the second level unit *Electrons and the nucleus*.)

Background reading
Conduction of electricity through gases, by J. Beynon.

Gases at normal temperatures and pressures are generally very good insulators. In fact, air needs about 25 kV to cause a spark to jump 1 cm between two rounded electrodes. (Think of the implications of this during a lightning flash!) In order for a gas to conduct, it must be ionised.

Q 3.16 Self-assessment question
State at least two ways in which a gas can be ionised.■

Current-potential difference relationships

When a p.d. is applied between two electrodes in an ionised gas, a force will be exerted on the positive ions and electrons. There will be a movement of charge — positive ions towards the cathode and electrons towards the anode.

Suppose that the air between two parallel plates P and Q (figure 3.4) is ionised, e.g. by the radiation from a radioactive source. The ionising current can be measured by means of a sensitive detector. The way in which the current varies, if the p.d. is increased, is shown in figure 3.5.

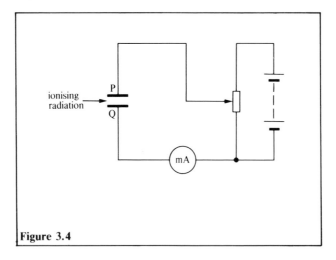

Figure 3.4

E Experiment EP 13 (optional)
Current–p.d. relationship for a gas
In this experiment you will investigate the conduction of electricity through neon gas.

Q 3.17 Study question
In figure 3.5, there are three regions of interest on the curve: OA, BC and CD. By considering the number of available electrons and positive ions, account for:
(a) how conduction occurs in the region OA,
(b) the steady increase in current in the region OA,
(c) the plateau region BC,
(d) the rapid increase in current in the region CD.■

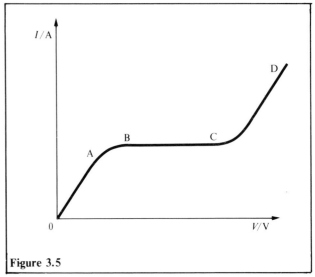

Figure 3.5

Q 3.18 Self-assessment question
Compare and contrast the conduction of electricity in metals, electrolytes and gases.■

The effect of reducing pressure

A very large p.d. is needed at atmospheric pressure to produce a current, in the form of a spark. However, if the pressure is reduced, so removing many atoms, it is much easier to cause conduction. The result is a steady current, which is called 'gas discharge' as opposed to the spark type of conduction at a high p.d. and atmospheric pressure. Associated with this gas discharge are luminous effects which change as the pressure varies.

Q **3.19 Study question**
Why is it easier for a gas to conduct as its pressure is reduced? Consider the distance travelled between collisions, the speeds that atoms or molecules attain and the effect of collisions.■

Q **3.20 Study question**
(a) Describe what happens in a gas-filled tube, with a fixed p.d. applied across it, as its pressure is reduced.
(b) Outline an application of a gas discharge tube.■

Although discharge (or cold cathode) tubes are seldom used in the laboratory these days, they have played an important role in the development of our understanding of the behaviour of electrons. The main problem associated with such tubes is their low efficiency. If we try to increase their efficiency, by increasing the p.d. applied, X-rays are produced, making the device a health hazard. This naturally limits their application.

Questions on objectives

1   Explain briefly how electricity is conducted through a solution of copper sulphate.

(objective 4)

2   The graphs in figure 3.6 show the relationship between the applied p.d. and current for
(a) a solution of copper sulphate using copper electrodes at constant temperature,
(b) a dilute solution of sulphuric acid using platinum electrodes at constant temperature.
Explain the shape of each graph.

(objective 5)

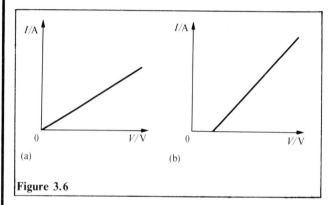

Figure 3.6

3   Explain what is meant by the statement:
'The Faraday constant is equal to $96\,000\ \mathrm{C\,mol^{-1}}$'.

(objective 2)

4   (a) Explain the meaning of each of the underlined terms in the following paragraph.
Copper is a metal that can be refined by electrolysis. The electrolyte is an aqueous solution of copper sulphate and sulphuric acid. The anodes are slabs of impure copper and the cathodes are thin sheets of very pure copper which gradually thicken during electrolysis.
(b) Explain the chemical changes that occur during the process of electrolysis.

(objectives 1 and 4)

5   Using nothing but the data listed below, calculate:
(a) the electric charge which liberates one mole of electrons in electrolysis,
(b) the mass of hydrogen liberated by the passage of one coulomb,
(c) the number of atoms in one mole of aluminium.
The magnitude of the electronic charge $e = 1.60 \times 10^{-19}\,\mathrm{C}$.
Mass of aluminium deposited by the passage of $1\ \mathrm{C} = 9.3 \times 10^{-8}\,\mathrm{kg}$.
Mass of aluminium atom: mass of hydrogen atom $= 27:1$.
The aluminium ion is $\mathrm{Al^{3+}}$.

(objectives 7 and 8)

An introduction to electronics

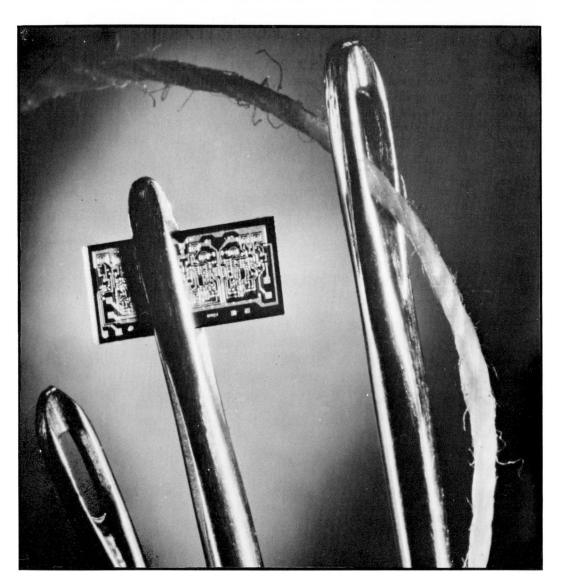

Aim

The aim of this chapter is to explain the electrical behaviour of semiconducting materials and develop an understanding of the action of *n*-type and *p*-type materials in a junction diode and a transistor.

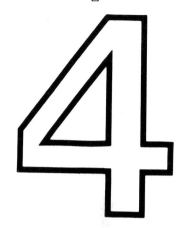

Objectives

When you have completed the work in this chapter you should be able to:

1 Use the following scientific terms correctly:
donor atom, acceptor atom, doping, free electron, hole, majority carriers, minority carriers, intrinsic semiconductor, extrinsic semiconductor, n-type, p-type, forward bias, reverse bias, $p-n$ junction diode, junction transistor.

2 Define and use the following scientific term:
forward current transfer ratio (current amplification factor or current gain).

3 Explain, in terms of valence electrons,
(a) what is meant by intrinsic and extrinsic semiconduction,
(b) how and why the electrical properties of an intrinsic semiconductor vary with temperature,
(c) what are meant by n-type and p-type semiconductors.

4 Explain the behaviour of a $p-n$ junction and its use as a rectifier.

5 (a) Perform and describe an experiment to determine the current–p.d. characteristic of a $p-n$ junction.
(b) Sketch and explain the forward and reverse characteristics of a $p-n$ junction.

6 Explain the action of the $n-p-n$ junction transistor and its operation as a current amplifier.

7 (a) Perform and describe an experiment to determine the characteristics of an $n-p-n$ junction transistor in a common-emitter connection.
(b) Sketch and explain the collector, base and transfer characteristics of an $n-p-n$ junction transistor.
(c) Show how the forward current transfer ratio can be obtained from the collector characteristics.

8 Describe and explain the use of the $n-p-n$ junction transistor in a common-emitter voltage amplifier circuit.

9 EXTENSION
Discuss in terms of the band theory the electrical properties of metals, insulators and semiconductors.

10 EXTENSION
Explain, in terms of valence electrons, the behaviour of a Zener diode.

11 EXTENSION
Define the terms input resistance and output resistance of a transistor and show how they can be obtained from the base and collector characteristics respectively.

12 EXTENSION
Describe and explain the use of an $n-p-n$ junction transistor as a switch.

13 EXTENSION
Explain the structure and action of a field-effect transistor.

Experiments in chapter 4

EP 14 Characteristics of a junction diode
(1 hour)
EP 15 Principle of the transistor
(1 hour)
EP 16 Characteristics of an $n-p-n$ transistor
(1 hour)
EP 17 Transistor amplifier
(1½ hours)
EP 18 EXTENSION
Switching action of a transistor
(¾ hour)

Study time: 2½ weeks

References

Bennet	Chapter 14
Brown	Chapter 11
Duncan FWA	Chapter 11
Nelkon	Chapter 42
Whelan	Chapter 61

4.1 Semiconductors

The invention of the transistor in 1948, by the American physicists John Bardeen, Walter Brattain and William Shockley, led to the creation of the modern semiconductor industry with a world-wide turnover of several billion pounds. The products of this industry have revolutionised computing and telecommunications. In the 1950s electronic computers contained thousands of vacuum tubes or valves, and special buildings were designed to house them. Today, a computer can be designed to fit into your pocket!

In this chapter we will first consider the concept of the semiconductor and develop a simple theory to account for the behaviour of n-type and p-type semiconducting materials (you do not need to know about the details of their manufacture). Secondly, we will see how these materials are used to make special electronic devices such as the junction diode and the junction transistor and find out something about their behaviour. Finally, the applications of these devices in simple electronic circuits are considered.

Semiconductors at room temperature, as their name suggests, are materials which have a conductivity between that of good insulators and good conductors. Figure 4.1 shows the range of conductivities in some typical materials. In addition, it is found that many insulators become semiconductors as their temperature is raised, so making the dividing lines between the categories somewhat blurred.

What is it that makes a material a semiconductor as opposed to a conductor? What are the factors that determine its conductivity? What are the effects of adding impurity atoms to the material? These are some of the questions that we shall answer in this section.

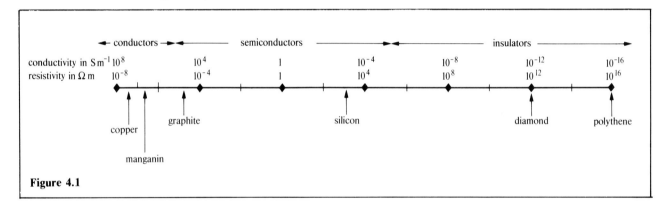

Figure 4.1

Intrinsic semiconductors

In the first chapter of this unit you found out that metals are able to conduct because they contain a large number of 'free' or conduction electrons, which are loosely attached to the metallic ions comprising the metal. When an electric field is applied the conduction electrons drift through the crystal lattice. On the other hand, in a material such as polythene, all the electrons are strongly bound to the atoms and cannot easily be detached. (Even though this model of electron flow is a simplified view, it is useful as a first approach. A fuller explanation of conduction based on energy considerations is mentioned in an extension at the end of this section.)

A silicon atom has four electrons (sometimes referred to as the valence electrons) in the outer shell, which are shared with the valence electrons of neighbouring atoms to form *covalent bonds*. This is represented in figure 4.2 by the two broken lines which join each atom to its neighbour.

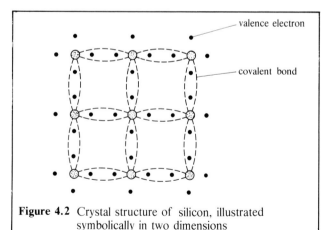

Figure 4.2 Crystal structure of silicon, illustrated symbolically in two dimensions

At room temperature, a few electrons may acquire sufficient energy from the vibration of the atoms in the crystal lattice to detach themselves from the parent atom. These electrons behave like the conduction electrons in a metal. This situation is illustrated in figure 4.3. Each valence electron that has 'escaped' from the parent atom creates a site in the atom which is positively charged. This 'vacant site' is called a *hole*. This hole may be filled by a valence electron from a neighbouring bond and so another hole is created at a different place in the lattice. Thus, although a valence electron is moving, we can consider that a hole with a positive charge is moving in the opposite direction.

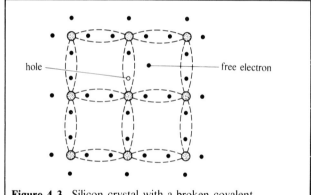

Figure 4.3 Silicon crystal with a broken covalent bond

In the absence of an electric field, the conduction electrons and the holes will wander at random throughout the material. Also, a hole may be refilled by a conduction electron. This process is known as *recombination*. At a given temperature, however, the rate at which holes are created is equal to the rate at which they are filled.

Semiconductors which have a high state of purity are called *intrinsic* semiconductors. The conduction in such semiconductors is due to charge carriers that have originated from the atoms of the semiconductor. The material is said to have intrinsic conduction.

Q 4.1 Self-assessment question
Explain the following statement:
'When a potential difference is applied across a material such as silicon there will be a net drift of conduction electrons in one direction while holes, which behave as positive charges, move in the opposite direction.'■

Q 4.2 Self-assessment question
To detach valence electrons from the parent atoms and, at the same time, create holes in the covalent bonds between the atoms, it is necessary to supply some form of energy to the semiconductor. State at least two ways in which this may be achieved. What effect does this have on the resistivity and/or conductivity of the material? Give reasons for your answer.■

Q 4.3 Self-assessment question

What information can you obtain from figure 4.4 about the electrical properties of intrinsic semiconductors? ■

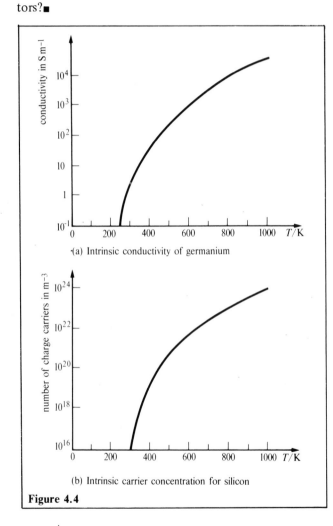

(a) Intrinsic conductivity of germanium

(b) Intrinsic carrier concentration for silicon

Figure 4.4

Extrinsic semiconductors

The number of available charge carriers in an intrinsic semiconductor is relatively small, but these numbers can be increased by adding suitable impurity atoms. The resulting material that is formed is known as an *extrinsic* semiconductor. The majority of charge carriers are provided by the impurity atoms (i.e. provided by an external source).

An *n*-type material is obtained when impurity atoms which have five valence or bonding electrons, e.g. phosphorus, are introduced. This is illustrated in figure 4.5.

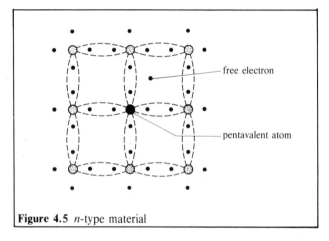

Figure 4.5 *n*-type material

The impurity atom is known as the *donor*, because the impurity gives free electrons as charge carriers to the crystal lattice. A *p*-type material is produced by adding atoms which have three valence electrons, e.g. indium, as shown in figure 4.6. In this case the impurity atom is known as the *acceptor*, because the impurity accepts valence electrons from neighbouring atoms which increases the number of positive holes in the crystal lattice.

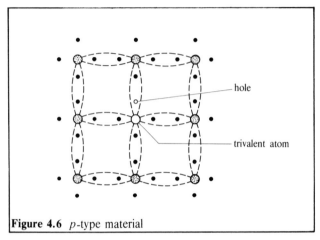

Figure 4.6 *p*-type material

The impurity atoms are introduced into the intrinsic semiconductor only in small quantities (1 atom of impurity to about 10^6 atoms of the material). This is all that is needed to have very significant results.

Q 4.4 Study question

Explain how the addition of impurity atoms increases the conductivity of *n*-type and *p*-type semiconductors. Your account should include reference to electrons, positive charge carriers, holes and covalent bonds. You should also distinguish between the majority and minority charge carriers in each type of semiconductor, explain the significance of the terms *n*-type and *p*-type, and why the doped material is electrically neutral. (You need not give an explanation in terms of energy levels and band theory.) ■

The features of *n*-type and *p*-type materials can be summarised as follows.

n-type semiconductors contain donor impurity atoms.
The *majority* charge carriers are *free electrons*.
The *minority* charge carriers are *holes*.

p-type semiconductors contain acceptor impurity atoms.
The *majority* charge carriers are *holes*.
The *minority* charge carriers are *free electrons*.

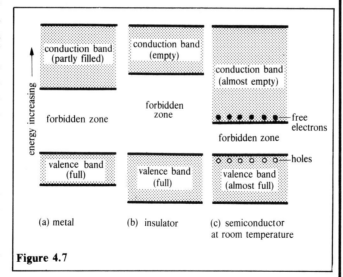
4.2 The junction diode

A junction diode is made from a single crystal of intrinsic semiconducting material. Impurity atoms are introduced so that one side of it is *n*-type and the other *p*-type. Thus a *p*-type germanium crystal may be grown by adding a minute concentration of indium atoms to the molten germanium. After growth has proceeded for a time, phosphorus atoms are introduced in such concentration as to overcompensate the indium atoms present so that the remainder of the crystal grows *n*-type.

Q 4.6 Self-assessment question
Why does the addition of indium and phosphorus atoms produce *p*-type or *n*-type material respectively?■

In order to understand the properties of the *p*–*n* junction diode we must consider what happens at the boundary of the *n*-type and the *p*-type materials. This is shown diagrammatically in figure 4.8. The donor ion is indicated by a plus sign, because after the impurity atom 'donates' an electron it becomes a positive ion. The acceptor ion is indicated by a negative sign, because after the impurity atom 'accepts' the electron it becomes a negative ion. When the junction is created there is a diffusion of electrons and holes near the junction, with the result that a region called the *depletion layer* is formed.

Figure 4·8 A *p*–*n* junction

Q **4.7 Study question**

Use your text books to make notes, based on the following questions, on the electrical behaviour of a *p*−*n* junction in terms of its structure.

(a) In which directions would you expect the electrons and holes to move?

(b) What is the effect of this movement?

(c) Why is it that the charges do not keep moving?

(d) Explain what is meant by the depletion layer.■

Rectifying properties

One important use of the *p*−*n* junction diode is as a rectifier, a device which allows current to pass in one direction only.

E **Experiment EP 14**
Characteristics of a junction diode

The aim of this experiment is to find out how the current through a junction diode depends upon the applied potential difference.

A *p*−*n* junction allows a current of the order of milli-amperes to pass in one direction. In the opposite direction there is only a very small current, of the order of microamperes. Typical characteristic curves for silicon and germanium junction diodes are shown in figure 4.9.

Q **4.8 Self-assessment question**

(a) Describe the forward characteristics shown in figure 4.9 in words.

(b) Describe the reverse characteristics in words.

(c) What are the significant differences between silicon and germanium diodes?■

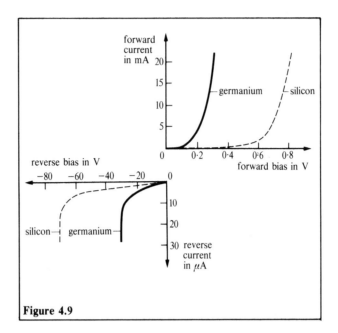

Figure 4.9

How can we account for this important property of the junction diode? When the junction is formed, diffusion of electrons from the *n*-type and holes from the *p*-type across the junction results in a potential difference (potential barrier) across the junction, which is positive on the *n*-side and negative on the *p*-side. We can represent this situation by means of a fictitious cell, shown by the dotted lines in figure 4.10. (Note that this is not a true e.m.f., because there is no source of energy. In fact, it resembles a charged capacitor rather than a cell.)

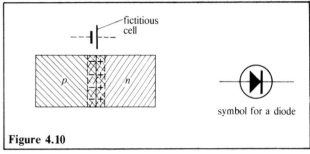

Figure 4.10

Forward bias

Now let us consider what happens when a source of e.m.f. is connected across the junction as shown in figure 4.11. The positive terminal of the battery is connected to the *p*-type and the negative terminal to the *n*-type. It is said to have *forward bias*.

The external source of e.m.f. will set up a p.d. across the *p*−*n* junction which opposes the p.d. of the fictitious cell, and a current will pass.

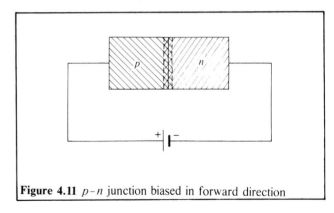

Figure 4.11 *p*−*n* junction biased in forward direction

Q **4.9 Self-assessment question**
(a) What effect does the applied p.d. have on the potential barrier?
(b) What happens as the applied p.d. is gradually increased and becomes greater than the barrier p.d.?
(c) In which directions do the electrons and holes flow?■

Reverse bias

Having examined the effect of connecting a battery so as to oppose the potential barrier, suppose that it is now connected to assist the barrier or fictitious cell. The negative terminal of the battery is therefore connected to the *p*-type region and the positive terminal to the *n*-type region, as shown in figure 4.12. The *p–n* junction is said to be *reverse biased* and no majority carriers will flow.

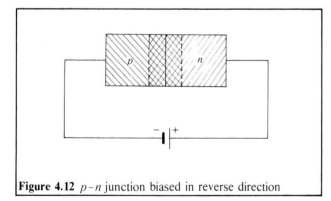

Figure 4.12 *p-n* junction biased in reverse direction

Q **4.10 Self-assessment question**
(a) Why does the potential barrier across the junction increase when a reverse bias is applied?
(b) Why is the drift of majority carriers (electrons from *n*-type, holes from *p*-type) prevented?■

This increased potential barrier prevents any drift of majority charge carriers, but in practice when a *p–n* junction is reverse biased, a very small reverse or leakage current passes. This is due to the presence in the crystal of a small number of minority charge carriers. In an *n*-type material holes are minority carriers, whereas in a *p*-type material electrons are the minority carriers.

Q **4.11 Self-assessment question**
How do the intrinsic charge carriers account for a small leakage current?■

Breakdown potential difference

If the p.d. is increased, a point is reached when the minority charge carriers acquire sufficient energy (from the intense electric field across the depletion layer) to ionise the lattice atoms by collision. The electrons which are produced by this ionisation are themselves accelerated and cause further ionisation. This *avalanche effect* results in a rapid increase in current.

Another mechanism also causes the release of electrons. At a certain p.d., known as the *Zener voltage*, the electric field is so high that valence electrons are torn away from their normal locations around the positive ions. This again results in a rapid increase in the current.

EXTENSION

Q **4.12 Study question**
Make brief notes on the Zener (or voltage regulator) diode. Explain, with the aid of a circuit diagram, how a Zener diode can be used to provide a steady p.d. across a load, despite the fact that both the input p.d. and load resistance can vary.■

4.3 The junction transistor

The junction transistor consists of *either* a thin region of p-type material sandwiched between two n-type regions (called an n–p–n transistor) *or* a region of n-type material between two p-type regions (called a p–n–p transistor). The transistor has three parts, the *collector*, the *emitter* and the *base*, shown diagrammatically in figure 4.13 together with the circuit symbols. The arrows indicate the direction of the conventional current through the transistor. We shall only be concerned with the n–p–n junction transistor.

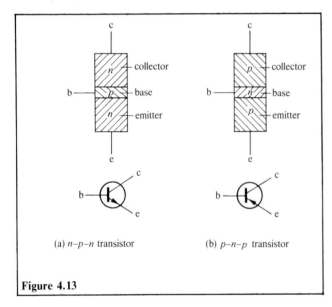

(a) n–p–n transistor   (b) p–n–p transistor

Figure 4.13

The base region is very thin (about 10^{-2} mm thick) and is lightly doped to give a small number density of hole (positive) charge carriers. The regions on either side are heavily doped to give a larger number density of electron (negative) charge carriers.

Q 4.13 Self-assessment question
What can you say about the resistivity of the n-type region compared to the p-type region? Give a reason for your answer. ■

Action

The n–p–n transistor can be regarded as two p–n diodes placed back-to-back. It is operated with one junction biased in the forward direction and the other in the reverse direction (figure 4.14).

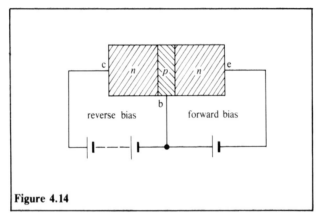

reverse bias   forward bias

Figure 4.14

E Experiment EP 15
Principle of the transistor
In this experiment you will find out how the current in the collector circuit depends upon the current in the base circuit.

Transistors show the following behaviour:
1 The transistor does not appear to pass any current in the collector circuit unless a current passes through the base circuit.
2 The current in the base circuit is very small compared with that in the collector circuit.
3 A small change in the size of the base current produces a much larger change in the collector current.

Q 4.14 Study question
Make notes, based on the following questions, on the action of the transistor.
(a) When the base region of the n–p–n transistor is made positive with respect to the emitter, electrons flow from the n-type emitter to the p-type base across the emitter–base junction. Explain why. (Consider the forward action of the p–n junction.)
(b) Consider what happens in the base region. Explain why only a few electrons recombine with the positive holes and why the majority pass into the collector region.
(c) Explain why there is no movement of electrons from the collector to the base.
(d) Explain why there is a small current in the base circuit.
(e) Why is the base lightly doped compared to the emitter? ■

In a typical silicon transistor a current of about 5 mA may flow through the emitter–base junction. About one per cent of this current (0.05 mA) passes through the base circuit and 4.95 mA passes through the collector circuit. In symbols,

$$I_e = I_b + I_c$$

where I_e, I_b and I_c are the currents passing into the emitter, base and collector connections respectively.

Q 4.15 Self-assessment question
Copy figure 4.14 and show clearly the direction of the electron flow and the direction of the conventional current to the emitter, base and collector connections.∎

Q 4.16 Self-assessment question
(a) Why are the terms emitter and collector appropriate words?
(b) What is symbolised by the arrow in a transistor symbol?∎

Q 4.17 Self-assessment question
The word transistor is derived from 'transfer of resistance'. Explain, in terms of the action of the transistor, why this is an appropriate name.∎

4.4 Transistor characteristics
In this section we shall look at the electrical characteristics of the transistor. Circuit designers make use of these characteristics to gain the data required to incorporate a transistor into a required application. The characteristics take a variety of forms, but they all illustrate how the various currents and potential differences depend upon each other.

Q 4.18 Self-assessment question
Figure 4.15 shows one way of connecting a transistor into a circuit.
(a) Why do you think this is called a common-emitter circuit?
(b) What physical quantities are represented by each of the symbols?∎

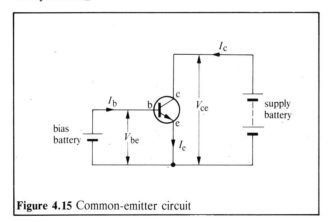

Figure 4.15 Common-emitter circuit

You may come across other arrangements in which *either* the base *or* the collector are common. We shall only be concerned with the common-emitter circuit from now on.

E Experiment EP 16
Characteristics of an $n-p-n$ transistor
In this experiment you will examine the relationship between the collector current, the base current and the potential difference between the collector and the emitter.

Collector characteristics
The collector (or output) characteristics are shown in figure 4.16 for a typical silicon transistor.

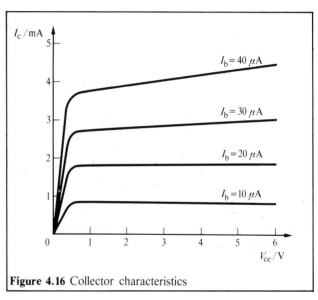

Figure 4.16 Collector characteristics

Q 4.19 Self-assessment question
(a) Above a collector potential of about 1.0 V, what does the collector current mainly depend on?
(b) How does the collector current depend on the collector potential when this has low values?∎

The transfer characteristic

The transfer characteristic shown in figure 4.17 shows that for a fixed value of V_{ce} there is an almost linear relationship between the collector current and the base current.

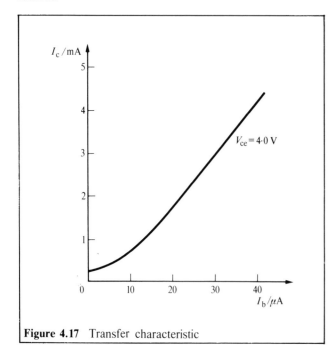

Figure 4.17 Transfer characteristic

Q **4.20 Self-assessment question**
How do the collector and transfer characteristics show that a small change in the base current causes a large change in the collector current?■

Q **4.21 Self-assessment question**
Why do you think that the relation between I_c and I_b is called a transfer characteristic?■

Base (input) characteristic

This characteristic tells us something about the way in which the base current depends upon the p.d. between the base and the emitter for a fixed value of collector–emitter p.d. A typical curve for a silicon $n-p-n$ junction transistor is shown in figure 4.18.

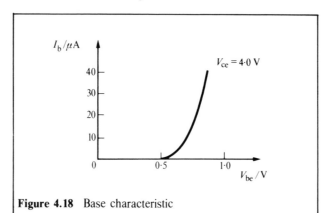

Figure 4.18 Base characteristic

Q **4.22 Self-assessment question**
State and explain the main features of the curve shown in figure 4.18.■

Q **4.23 Self-assessment question**
If you carry out an experiment to find the relation between I_b and V_{be}, why is it important to have a very high resistance voltmeter? Draw a diagram showing how it should be connected in the base circuit in relation to the microammeter.■

Using the characteristics

The characteristics of a transistor are used to determine the transistor parameters (the figures which describe the performance of a transistor). The most important one is concerned with the current gain of the transistor. It tells us how a small change in the base current affects the collector current at a certain value of collector–emitter potential difference and is called the *small signal forward current transfer ratio*. This is denoted by the symbol h_{fe}, where the subscript f denotes 'forward' and e denotes a common-emitter circuit.

Note: h_{fe} used to be called the current amplification factor, β. You will still find this term used in many text books and examination papers.

For a fixed value of V_{ce}

$$h_{fe} = \frac{\Delta I_c}{\Delta I_b}$$

where ΔI_b is a small change in the base current and ΔI_c is the corresponding change in the collector current. This parameter can be obtained from the linear part of the collector characteristics.

Q 4.24 Self-assessment question

Figure 4.19 shows a simplified graph of the output characteristics of a transistor. The line AB has been drawn at a certain value of collector–emitter potential difference.

(a) For this value of V_{ce}, what is the value of the collector current when the base current is (i) $I_{b,1}$ and (ii) $I_{b,2}$?

(b) Show that

$$h_{fe} = \frac{I_{c,2} - I_{c,1}}{I_{b,2} - I_{b,1}} . \blacksquare$$

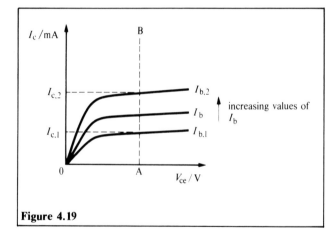

Figure 4.19

We can also obtain information about the current gain of a transistor from the transfer characteristics.

Q 4.25 Development question

Figure 4.20 shows a graph of the transfer characteristic of a transistor. The line AB has been drawn at a certain value of base current. Copy this graph and use it to show how you would obtain the small signal forward current transfer ratio (or current amplification factor). $\blacksquare$

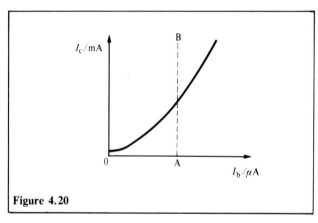

Figure 4.20

The graph of I_c against I_b is almost a straight line which goes almost through the origin. The ratio of I_c/I_b for a particular value of V_{ce} is called the *static value of the forward current transfer ratio*. It is denoted by h_{FE}, and h_{FE} and h_{fe} are almost equal. In practice they can be thought of as being equal.

Q 4.26 Study question

Make a brief summary of the characteristics of the $n{-}p{-}n$ junction transistor. Your account should include details of how you would obtain the characteristics by means of an experiment (include a circuit diagram), appropriate curves and a comment on their features. $\blacksquare$

EXTENSION

Q 4.27 Study question

Two other parameters of a transistor are
(a) the input resistance,
(b) the output resistance.

Explain how these two parameters are obtained from the base and collector characteristics respectively. $\blacksquare$

4.5 The transistor as an amplifier

Current amplification

In sections 4.3 and 4.4 we have seen how a small current in the base circuit of the transistor controls a much larger current in the collector circuit. The junction transistor is a *current controlled* device and amplifies the current directly. A small alternating input p.d. will cause an alternating current to be superposed on the steady base current. This results in an amplified alternating current to be superposed on the steady collector current.

Figure 4.21 shows how we make use of the linear region of the transfer characteristic when we use the transistor as an amplifier. The changes in I_b will produce changes in I_c. Because of the linear relation between I_b and I_c, the changes in I_c will have the same frequency as those in I_b, but much larger amplitude.

This imposes two limitations on the input signal:
(a) it must change about an average base current I_b, known as the *bias current*,
(b) its variation on either side of the bias current must not be so large that it leaves the linear part of the characteristic.

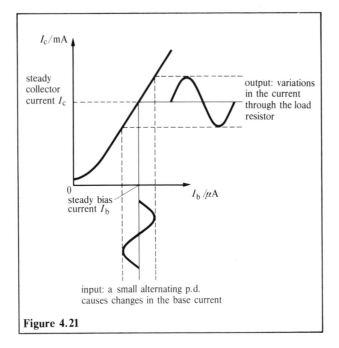

Figure 4.21

Q 4.28 Self-assessment question
(a) Using the data given in the table below, plot a graph of the collector current I_c against the base current I_b.

$I_b/\mu A$	I_c/mA	$I_b/\mu A$	I_c/mA
0.0	0.1	140.0	7.0
20.0	0.6	180.0	9.0
50.0	2.0	210.0	9.9
80.0	3.6	240.0	10.2
110.0	5.3	270.0	10.4

(b) Use your graph to find a value for the small signal forward current transfer ratio for a steady bias current of 125 μA.
(c) What would be the output peak-to-peak current for an input sine wave of 80 μA peak-to-peak biased at 125 μA?
(d) What would be the effect of moving the bias point to a steady base current of 50 μA?■

The load resistor

If the supply battery is connected directly to the collector the p.d. between the collector and emitter will be fixed. It will not respond to variations in the base current, so the variations in current cannot be used. Therefore we have to arrange for the potential V_{ce} at the collector to vary. This is achieved by connecting a resistor R_c, called the *load resistor*, in series between the collector and the positive terminal of the supply battery as shown in figure 4.22.

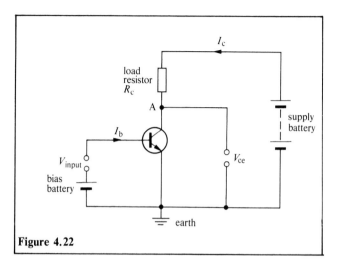

Figure 4.22

Q 4.29 Development question

(a) Show that the potential of the collector V_{ce} is given by

$$V_{ce} = V - R_c I_c$$

where V is the p.d. across the terminals of the supply and I_c the collector current.

(b) What happens to the potential at A when there is (i) a small increasing change and (ii) a small decreasing change of current in the base circuit? Give a reason for your answer.■

Q 4.30 Self-assessment question

Calculate the value of the load resistor from the following data: h_{fe} = 100, I_b = 10 μA, V_{ce} = 4.0 V, V = 9.0 V.■

Biasing the base

So far, we have used a separate battery to bias the base (that is, to provide the required p.d. between the base and emitter). In a transistor receiver there is only one battery — this is obviously more convenient. How can we bias the base without using a separate battery? One method is to connect the base to the supply battery through a high resistance R_b (figure 4.23).

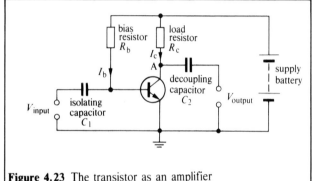

Figure 4.23 The transistor as an amplifier

Q 4.31 Development question*

Show that the potential of the base is given by

$$V_{be} = V - R_b I_b$$

where V is the supply voltage and I_b the base current.■

Q 4.32 Self-assessment question

Using the data given in question 4.30, calculate a value for the bias resistance if the required value of V_{be} is to be 0.7 V.■

The way in which the potential at the collector varies when a small alternating p.d. has been applied across the input terminals of the amplifier circuit is shown in figure 4.24.

Q 4.33 Self-assessment question

What do the graphs shown in figure 4.24 tell us about the phase relationship between the input and output signals? (Are they in step or out of step — if so, by how much?)■

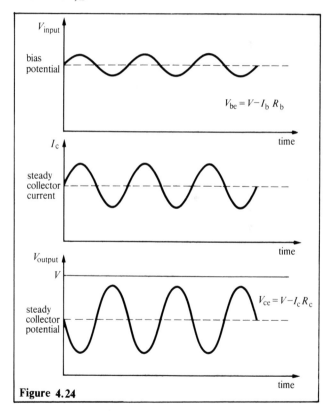

Figure 4.24

Decoupling capacitor

In practice, an amplifier has several stages of amplification, the output of the first transistor being passed on to the base of the next transistor.

Q 4.34 Self-assessment question
What would be the effect of connecting the collector of the first transistor directly to the base of the second transistor?∎

In order to prevent the potential of the collector being applied directly to the base of the next transistor, a capacitor C_2 is connected as shown in figure 4.23. This capacitor is called a *decoupling capacitor* or *blocking capacitor*. (The behaviour of capacitors is covered in the unit *Forces and fields*.)

The capacitor is charged by the battery and has a potential drop across it of V_{ce}. It therefore isolates the next base from the previous collector. However, when the potential at A varies, the capacitor allows the variation in potential and current to reach the base of the next transistor.

E Experiment EP 17
Transistor amplifier
The aim of this experiment is to construct a simple single-stage transistor amplifier. You will also measure the voltage gain of the circuit and examine the output p.d. using an oscilloscope.

Q 4.35 Study question
Make a summary of the action of the transistor as an amplifier. You should include an explanation of how a transistor can amplify a small alternating p.d., giving details of a practical amplifier and a circuit diagram.∎

Q 4.36 Self-assessment question
The resistance R of the cadmium sulphide (CdS) photo-conductive cell (figure 4.25) falls when the cell is illuminated.
(a) Explain why the relay will close when the illumination is increased.
(b) Calculate the approximate value of R at which the relay will close. (The relay closes when I_c is 20 mA. $h_{FE} = 120$. Assume that the p.d. between the base and emitter is negligible.)∎

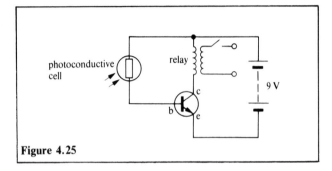

Figure 4.25

4.6 The transistor as a switch

In section 4.5 we have seen how the base and collector currents control the output p.d. of the transistor amplifier. When the input is high (i.e. a large current through the base circuit) the output is low (i.e. there is a large drop in p.d. across the load resistor), and vice versa. This property enables the transistor to be used as a switch. In fact, over 95% of all transistors that are manufactured are used in switching circuits in high-speed digital computers.

E **Experiment EP 18**
Switching action of a transistor
In this experiment you will find out the relationship between the input p.d. and the output p.d. of a transistor circuit.

Q **4.40 Self-assessment question**
The graph in figure 4.26 shows how the output p.d. of the transistor amplifier varies with the input p.d. for the circuit shown in figure 4.27.
(a) When the input p.d. is less than V_1, why is the output p.d. 6V?
(b) When the input p.d. is greater than V_2, why is the output p.d. almost 0 V?■

Figure 4.26 shows that
if $V_i = 0$ V (OFF), $V_o = 6$ V (ON)
and if $V_i = 6$ V (ON), $V_o =$ almost 0 V (OFF)
Thus, when the input is *switched 'on'* the output is *switched 'off'*.

Switches which have several inputs and hence various outputs are known as *gates*; they open and give an output only when certain input conditions are met.

Q **4.41 Study question**
The transistor is used as a switch in computers and control systems. How is it used in this field? You should consider the use of the transistor in NOR, OR and AND gates.■

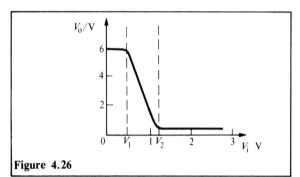

Figure 4.26

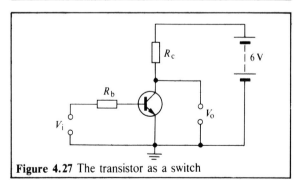

Figure 4.27 The transistor as a switch

4.7 The field-effect transistor

The field-effect transistor (f.e.t.) differs from the junction transistor in two respects.
1 The f.e.t. is a *voltage-controlled* device. The current through it is controlled by applying a bias potential to the control electrode. The junction transistor is a current-controlled device.
2 The current is carried through an f.e.t. by a drift of majority carriers only, hence its alternative name, a *unipolar* transistor. In the junction transistor the current is carried by the drift of both electrons and positive holes (a bipolar transistor).

The f.e.t. has three terminals, known as the source s, the gate g and the drain d, which are used in a similar way to the emitter, base and collector of a junction transistor. Figure 4.28 shows diagrammatically the construction of an *n*-channel f.e.t., together with the circuit symbol.

In use, the drain is kept at a positive potential relative to the source and the drain current I_d is controlled by making the potential at the gate negative relative to the source.

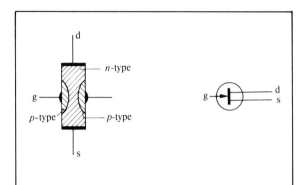

Figure 4.28 An *n*-channel field-effect transistor

Q **4.42 Study question**
(a) Make brief notes on the construction of an *n*-channel f.e.t. and explain its action.
(b) Describe an experiment to determine the drain and transfer characteristics of the f.e.t.
(c) Sketch and explain the drain and transfer characteristics.
(d) Explain how an f.e.t. can be used as an amplifier.■

Note: If an f.e.t. is available, carry out experiments to investigate the relation between the drain current and drain potential for fixed values of gate potential. Set up an amplifier circuit.

Questions on objectives

1 Explain what is meant by intrinsic conduction.

(objective 3)

2 Discuss in terms of valence electrons the effect of temperature on the conductivity of an intrinsic semiconductor.

(objective 3)

3 (a) What relationship does the graph in figure 4.29 show between the resistivity of silicon and impurity concentration?
(b) Explain this in terms of valence electrons.

(objective 3)

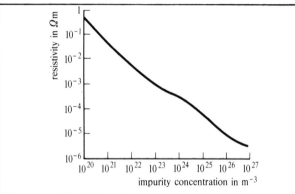

Figure 4.29 Resistivity of *n*-type silicon as a function of impurity concentration

4 (a) Draw a diagram to show a *p*–*n* junction connected so that it is forward biased.
(b) Draw a sketch graph to show the relationship between the applied p.d. and the forward current. Explain the shape of the graph.

(c) What is the cause of the leakage or reverse current when the *p*–*n* junction is reverse biased?
(d) Why is the leakage current greater for a germanium diode than for a silicon diode?

(objectives 4 and 5)

5 Figure 4.30 shows an *n*–*p*–*n* transistor and its associated power supplies. Explain why the current I_c is considerably greater than the current I_b.

(objective 6)

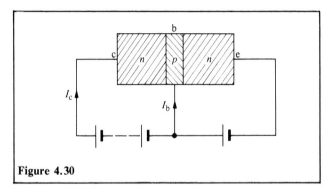

Figure 4.30

6 (a) Describe, giving a circuit diagram, the experiment you would perform to determine the collector characteristics of an *n*–*p*–*n* transistor in a common-emitter connection.
(b) Draw sketch graphs to show how (i) the collector current varies with the collector–emitter p.d. for a fixed base current, (ii) the collector current varies with the base current for a fixed collector–emitter p.d., and (iii) the base current varies with base potential for a fixed collector–emitter p.d.
(c) Explain the shape of the graph in each case.

(objective 7)

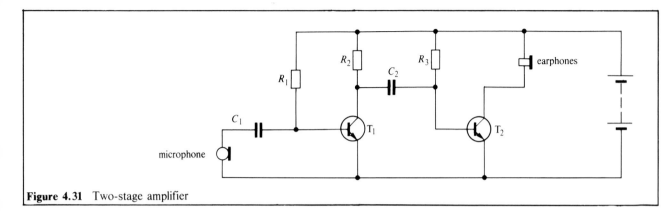

Figure 4.31 Two-stage amplifier

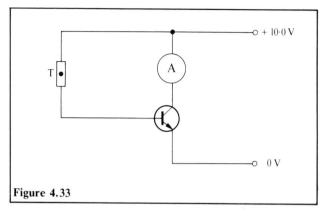

Figure 4.33

7 The circuit diagram shown in figure 4.31 shows a two-stage amplifier. Explain briefly the function of each of the components.

(objective 8)

8 Explain what is meant by the following statement. 'A transistor has a small signal forward current transfer ratio of 100.'

(objective 2)

9 The circuit shown in figure 4.32 shows a way of biasing a transistor using a fixed transistor. The p.d. between the collector and emitter of the transistor is 3.0 V. The transistor's forward current transfer ratio, h_{FE}, is 60. Calculate the current passing through the base of the transistor and a suitable value for the resistance R. Assume that the p.d. between the base and emitter is negligible.

(objective 8)

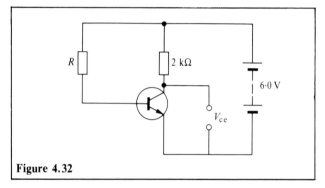

Figure 4.32

10 The circuit in figure 4.33 is a simple design for a resistance thermometer. The component T is a thermistor whose resistance varies from 500 kΩ to 10 kΩ for a temperature range from 0 °C to 50 °C. Calculate the range of the ammeter required if the forward current transfer ratio of the transistor is 100. Assume that the p.d. between the base and emitter is negligible.

(objective 8)

Experiment EP1 Investigating conductors

Aim

In this experiment you will find out the effect of varying the p.d. across the terminals of several boxes, each of which contains a different conducting device.

Apparatus

- 1.5 V dry cells and cell holder *or* l.t. variable power supply
- milliammeter, 0–100 mA (some more sensitive ammeters should also be available)
- voltmeter, 0–10 V
- two-terminal boxes
- leads

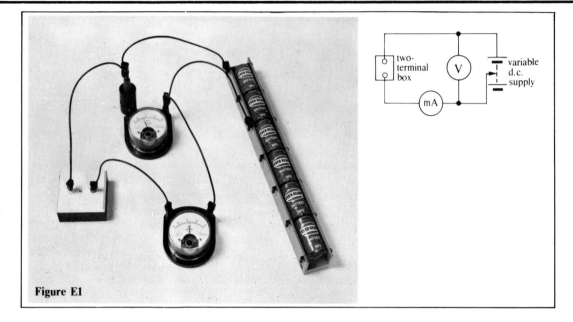

Figure E1

1   Set up a circuit for measuring potential differences and small currents, as shown in figure E1.

2   For each of the two-terminal boxes, obtain a series of values for the p.d. and the corresponding current. You should also try the effect of reversing the p.d. This will help you to distinguish between the different components.
Note. If the current is very small, you may need to use a more sensitive meter. Why do you start with the *least* sensitive meter or range?

3   Plot your results on suitable graphs. Which conductors obey Ohm's law?

4   Try to identify the devices in each of the boxes. Comment on the characteristics which helped you to recognise them.

Experiment EP2 Effect of temperature on resistance

Aim

In this experiment you are required to find out how temperature affects the ability of a material to conduct electricity. You are not required to make a detailed investigation, but from your observations to find the way in which the resistance of the material is affected by temperature. You will investigate three materials, a coil of copper wire, a carbon resistor and a thermistor (this is a device made from a semiconducting material).

Apparatus

1.5 V dry cells and cell holder
or l.t. variable power supply
ammeter, 0–1 A
milliammeter, 0–100 mA
• enamelled copper wire, 36 s.w.g.
• carbon resistor, 150 Ω
• thermistor
switch
beaker, 250 ml
aerosol freezer
clip component holder
leads

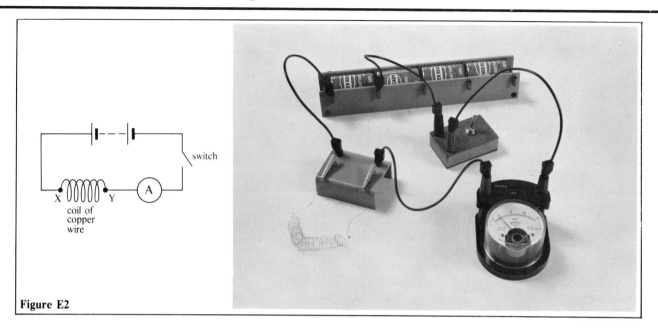

Figure E2

1 Wind about 3 metres of the copper wire into a coil. Connect the coil of wire and the ammeter in series with a low voltage supply of about 2 volts, as shown in figure E2.

2 Measure the current when the coil is
(a) in a tight bundle,
(b) laid out loosely on the bench,
(c) placed in hot water,
(d) placed in cold water,
(e) cooled by the aerosol freezer.

3 Repeat the experiment with the carbon resistor, using a milliammeter and a single 1.5 V dry cell.

4 Using the same circuit and procedure as for the carbon resistor, show that the thermistor gives a larger change of current for the same temperature range.

5 Comment on the observations that you have made. Include as much detail as your results allow about how temperature affects resistance in each case.

Experiment EP3 Internal resistance of a cell

Aim

In this experiment you will use a high resistance voltmeter to measure the p.d. across the terminals of a cell in two different circumstances. First you will measure it on open circuit, when no current is passing. Then you will measure the p.d. across the cell when the cell is delivering current to an external load. From your measurements you will obtain a value for the internal resistance of the cell.

Apparatus

- 1.5 V dry cell and cell holder
- voltmeter, 0–5 V (high resistance)
- ammeter, 0–1 A
- variable resistor, 0–15 Ω
- switch
- leads

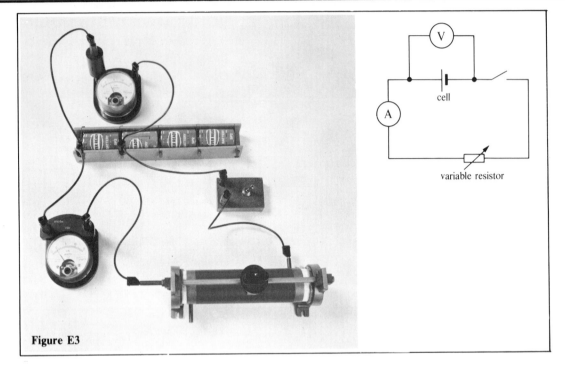

Figure E3

1   Set up the circuit as shown in figure E3, with the variable resistor at its maximum value.

2   With the switch S open, observe and record the reading on the voltmeter, E.

3   Close the switch and obtain and record five readings of the current I through the external resistance and the p.d. V across the cell, over the widest range possible. Open the switch after you have taken each set of readings. Why?
Note. When the cell is on open circuit the p.d. across its terminals is equal to its e.m.f.

4   You should have noticed that when the switch was closed there was a decrease in the voltmeter reading. What is a possible explanation of this observation?

5   Plot a graph of the p.d. V on the y-axis against the current I on the x-axis.

6   From your graph determine the value of V when $I = 0$.

7   Compare your value with the voltmeter reading E when the cell was on open circuit.

8   Use your graph to determine the internal resistance of the cell.

Experiment EP4 The cathode ray oscilloscope

Aim
The aim of this experiment is to use an oscilloscope to measure potential differences and time intervals, and to display wave-forms.

Apparatus
cathode ray oscilloscope
l.t. variable power supply
voltmeter, 0–10 V
variable resistance, 0–15 Ω
signal generator
leads

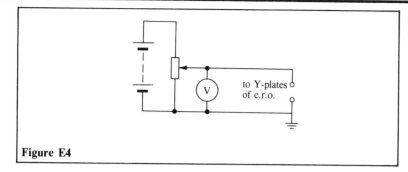

Figure E4

Measurement of potential difference
Note. Make sure you are familiar with the controls of the c.r.o. before starting this experiment. (Figure 2.12 describes the controls of a typical c.r.o. The manufacturer's handbook will give details for the particular oscilloscope you are using.)

1   Set up the circuit as shown in figure E4, with the time base of the c.r.o. switched off.

2   Adjust the c.r.o. so that the spot is focused at the centre of the screen.
Note. Turn down the brightness control until you are ready to take measurements, then turn it up, make the measurement, then reduce the brightness again.

3   Adjust the setting of the Y-gain control to a suitable value (e.g. 2 V cm^{-1}). Apply a series of known potential differences V to the Y-input and measure the corresponding deflection d of the spot.

4   Plot a graph of the deflection d against the applied p.d. V.

5   Does your graph confirm that the deflection is proportional to the applied p.d.?

6   Use your graph to calculate the deflection sensitivity of the c.r.o. (for the setting of the Y-gain control chosen in step 3) in mm per volt (mm V^{-1}). How does your value agree with the calibrated gain control?

Measurement of alternating potential difference
1   Connect the output of the signal generator to the Y-input of the c.r.o. Set the frequency of the generator at 50 Hz, with a sinusoidal output (this is usually indicated by a sine wave symbol on the signal generator).

2   Adjust the setting of the Y-gain control to a suitable value (e.g. 2 V cm^{-1}), with the time base switched off.

3   Adjust the output of the signal generator so that it produces a vertical line which just fits on the screen. For this setting of the output, measure the deflection and hence calculate the maximum value of the alternating p.d. (this value is also called the peak value).

4   Investigate the effect on the output of altering the frequency of the signal generator.

5   Calibrate the output control knob of the signal generator and determine whether it has a linear scale.

Measurement of frequency
1   Connect the signal generator to the Y-input. Set the frequency at 50 Hz.

2   Switch on the time base and set the trigger control to 'auto'.

3   Select a suitable time base setting (e.g. 5 ms per division).

4   Adjust the c.r.o. controls until you can measure the wavelength of the trace on the screen.

5   Calculate the time for a complete cycle and hence determine the frequency. Compare your calculated value with the setting on the signal generator.

6   Repeat steps 3 to 5 for frequency settings of 500 Hz, 5 kHz and 50 kHz. (An appropriate time base setting will have to be selected for each case.)

Experiment EP5 The potentiometer

Aim

In this experiment you will find out how the p.d. along a uniform wire depends upon the length of the wire, and consider the principles of the potentiometer circuit.

Apparatus

- accumulator (driver cell)
- switch
- slide-wire potentiometer
- jockey (sliding contact)
- voltmeter, 0–5 V or 0–3 V
- 1.5 V dry cell and cell holder
- galvanometer
- leads

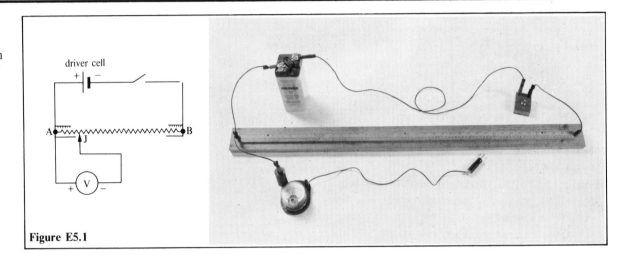

Figure E5.1

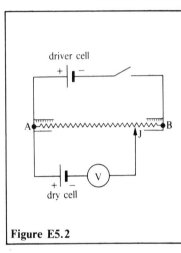

Figure E5.2

1   Using the accumulator as the driver cell, set up the circuit as shown in figure E5.1.

2   Close the switch and touch the sliding contact J to the potentiometer wire at a point near to the end A.

3   Observe and record the reading V on the voltmeter and the distance l between A and the contact J.

4   Move the contact point nearer B. Obtain and record a series of readings for the p.d. V across the wire and the length l of the wire. Use the whole range of the potentiometer wire. Which can you measure more accurately, l or V (that is, which has the smaller percentage error)?

5   Plot a graph of the p.d. V across the wire (y-axis) against the length l of wire (x-axis).

6   What can you conclude from your graph about the relationship between the p.d. across a part of the wire and the length of that part of the wire?

7   Connect a dry cell into the circuit as shown in figure E5.2 and place the sliding contact on the end B.

8   Move the contact towards A and locate the point J on the wire for which the reading on the voltmeter is zero. Record the balance length AJ.
Note. If you find difficulty in locating this position, check that you have connected the dry cell correctly. (The same terminal of each cell should be connected to A).

9   Replace the voltmeter by a galvanometer (figure E5.3) and check your *balance point*, that is, the position of the contact J on the wire for *zero* reading on the galvanometer.

10 From your graph of V against l, find the p.d. across the balance length. (At the balance point, the p.d. *across the galvanometer* is zero)

11 What can you say about the p.d. across the balance length and the p.d. across the terminals of the cell? (There is no current through the cell, so the p.d. across it is its open circuit p.d., that is, its e.m.f.)

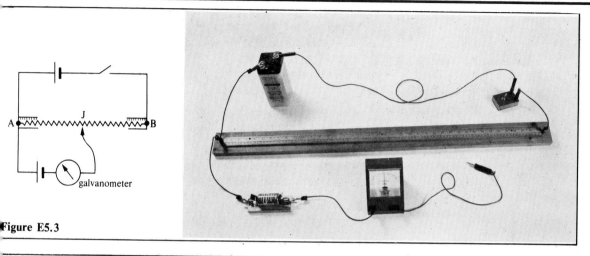

Figure E5.3

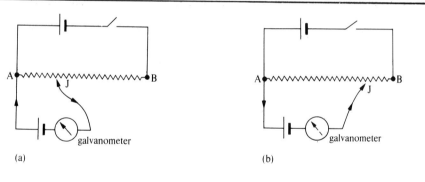

(a) (b)

igure E5.4

12 What is the value of the e.m.f. of the cell? How precise can you be? What limits the accuracy of your answer?

13 Explain why, when the contact J is placed near A (figure E5.4a), the current is in the direction JGA, but when the contact is placed near to B (figure E5.4b) it is in the direction AGJ.

14 Why is a galvanometer more suitable than a voltmeter for detecting the balance point?

Practical hints for potentiometer experiments

1 Check that the circuit is connected up so that the p.d. across the potentiometer wire is greater than the p.d.s that are being measured or compared. Do this by making certain that the galvanometer needle is deflected in *opposite directions* when the sliding contact is placed at opposite ends of the potentiometer wire.

If you *do* get deflections in opposite directions, then you will obtain a balance point.

If you *do not* get deflections in opposite directions, then check that the end A is a common terminal (usually positive) and/or increase the p.d. across the potentiometer wire by using a recently charged accumulator or more than one accumulator.

2 The balance point should be near to the end B. A variable resistor, in series with the potentiometer wire, can be adjusted to alter the p.d. across the potentiometer wire so that it is comparable with the p.d. that is being measured. This also allows several independent readings to be taken with different p.d.s across the potentiometer wire.

3 Avoid damaging the sensitive galvanometer. Only touch the potentiometer wire with the sliding contact momentarily until you are near the balance point. Protect the galvanometer by reducing its sensitivity with either a series resistor or a shunt. This should only be removed when you are near the balance point.

Experiment EP6 Internal resistance of a cell using a potentiometer

Aim

A source of electrical energy has an *internal resistance*, and when it delivers a current I, the p.d. across its terminals falls by Ir, where r is the internal resistance of the source. In this experiment you will gain experience in using a potentiometer circuit and measure the internal resistance of a cell.

Apparatus

- accumulator (driver cell)
- variable resistor, 0–15 Ω
- slide-wire potentiometer
- 1.5 V dry cell and cell holder
- resistance box, 0–50 Ω
- galvanometer
- protective resistor
- jockey (sliding contact)
- leads

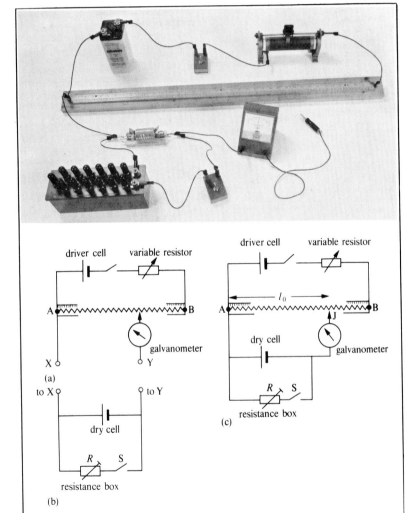

Figure E6

1 Set up the circuit as shown in figure E6. Before you begin, find out the maximum current which the resistance box coils will stand. Make sure you do not reduce the resistance below a safe value. *Note.* Read through the practical hints listed in experiment EP 5 before you start taking readings.

2 With the switch S *open*, find the balance length l_0 (taking the precautions noted in the practical hints).

3 Adjust the resistance R to a value of about 40 Ω. *Close* the switch and find the new balance length l. Open the switch when you have found the balance point.

4 Reduce the value of R and obtain and record a series of values for the resistance R and the corresponding balance length l.

5 Using these results, plot a suitable straight line graph and from it determine a value for the internal resistance of the dry cell.

Experiment EP7 Measuring resistance with a potentiometer

Aim

In this experiment you will determine the resistance of a resistor by comparing the p.d.s across an unknown and a known resistor when the same current passes through them.

Apparatus

slide-wire potentiometer
2 accumulators
2 variable resistors, 0–15 Ω
galvanometer
jockey (sliding contact)
protective resistor
unknown resistor
standard resistor
leads
2 switches

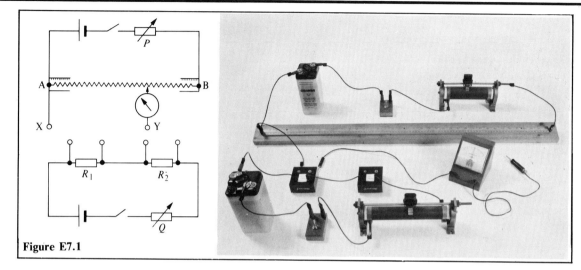

Figure E7.1

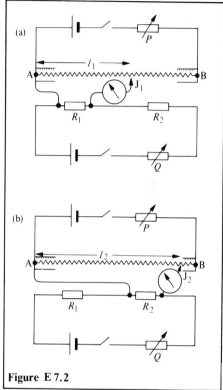

Figure E 7.2

1   Set up the circuits as shown in figure E7.1.
Note. The variable resistors P and Q will enable you to adjust the currents through the potentiometer wire and the two series resistors so that you obtain a balance point near the end of the potentiometer wire. Read through the practical hints in experiment EP 5 before taking readings.

2   Find the balance length l_1 when the potentiometer terminals XY are connected across R_1 (figure E7.2a).

3   Connect the potentiometer across the unknown resistance R_2 and find the balance point l_2, using the *same settings* of P and Q (figure E7.2b).

4   Repeat the experiment several times, each time using a different setting of the variable resistor Q to give a pair of values of the balance lengths (keep the setting of P constant).

5   Use your results to calculate the value of the unknown resistance R_2.

6   Estimate the percentage error in your value for the resistance.

7   Explain why this method can be made suitable for the measurement of low resistances.

Experiment EP8 Thermoelectric e.m.f. and temperature

Aim

A thermoelectric e.m.f. can be measured with a potentiometer. However, because the e.m.f. of the thermocouple is small, the potentiometer circuit has to be modified so that the p.d. across the potentiometer wire is of the order of millivolts. This is achieved by placing a high resistance R in series with the potentiometer wire.

Apparatus

- accumulator (driver cell)
- slide-wire potentiometer
- resistance box, 0–5000 Ω
- sensitive galvanometer (light beam)
- jockey (sliding contact)
- protective resistor
- copper-constantan thermo-couple
- switch
- leads
- 2 beakers, 250 ml
- thermometer, 0–360 °C
- sand bath
- tripod and gauze
- bunsen burner

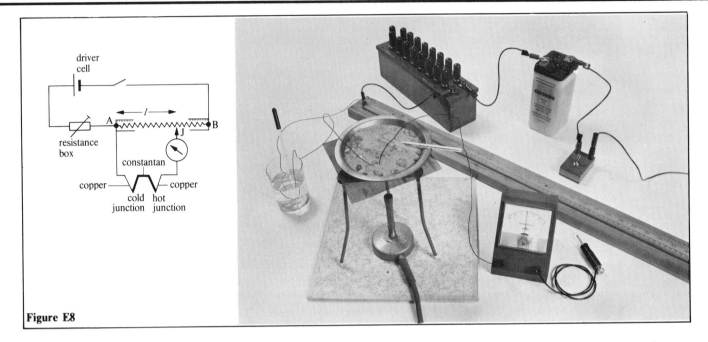

Figure E8

1   Set up the circuit as shown in figure E8.
Note. One junction of the thermocouple should be placed in a beaker containing melting ice (the temperature of this can be assumed to be 0 °C), the other junction in a sand bath. The resistance of the resistance box, R, should be about 1000 Ω. Read through the practical hints in experiment EP 5 before taking readings.

2   Heat the sand bath until the reading on the thermometer is about 300 °C.

3   Find the balance point of the thermoelectric e.m.f. along the potentiometer wire. Record the balance length AJ.
Note. Adjust the value of R so that the balance point is near to the end B of the potentiometer wire.

4   While you are locating this position, the temperature of the hot junction should be kept constant. How does the sand bath help you to achieve this?

5   Keeping the resistance R constant, obtain a series of values for the balance length l at different temperatures.

6   Plot a graph to show how the thermoelectric e.m.f. varies with temperature.

Experiment EP9 Measuring resistance with a metre bridge

Aim

In this experiment you will use a metre bridge to determine the value of an unknown resistance.

Apparatus

- metre bridge
- accumulator
- switch
- galvanometer
- protective resistor
- jockey (sliding contact)
- unknown resistor
- resistance box, 0–50 Ω
- variable resistor, 0–15 Ω
- thick leads for resistors

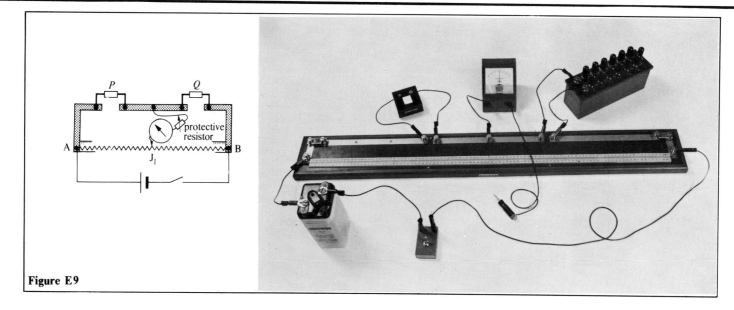

Figure E9

1 Connect up the circuit as shown in figure E9, with a protective resistance in series with the galvanometer.
Note. To ensure that you have connected the circuit correctly, touch each end of the metre wire with the sliding contact. The galvanometer should show deflections in opposite directions.

2 By trial and error, select a value for the known resistance Q so that a balance point J_1 is obtained near the centre of the wire.

3 When the balance point has been found to the nearest centimetre remove the protective resistor and locate the balance point as accurately as possible. Record the value of Q and the lengths AJ_1 and BJ_1.

4 Reverse the direction of the current to the bridge (by reversing the connections to the cell). Locate the new balance point J_2 and record the lengths AJ_2 and BJ_2.

5 Interchange the positions of P and Q, obtain a third balance point J_3, and record the lengths AJ_3 and BJ_3.

6 Reverse the current, locate a fourth balance point J_4, and record the lengths AJ_4 and BJ_4.

7 Find the mean of AJ_1, AJ_2, BJ_3 and BJ_4 (l_1) and the mean of BJ_1, BJ_2, AJ_3 and AJ_4 (l_2).

8 Calculate a value for the unknown resistance P from the equation
$$\frac{P}{Q} = \frac{l_1}{l_2}$$

9 Estimate the errors in the balance lengths l_1 and l_2.

10 Calculate the percentage error in P.

Experiment EP10 Temperature coefficient of resistance (optional)

Aim

In this experiment you will use a metre bridge to measure the resistance of a coil of copper wire over a range of temperatures, and from your results plot a graph from which the temperature coefficient of resistance of copper can be calculated.

Apparatus

- accumulator
- metre bridge
- jockey (sliding contact)
- resistance box, 0–50 Ω
- galvanometer
- protective resistor
- switch
- leads
- coil of copper wire
- thermometer, 0–110 °C
- beaker, 250 ml
- bunsen burner
- tripod and gauze
- ice

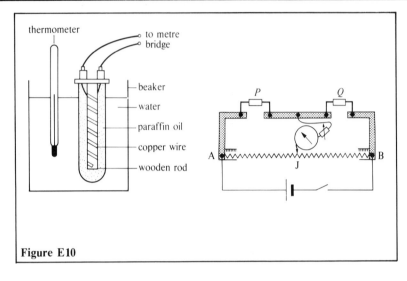

Figure E10

1   Connect up the metre bridge circuit as shown in figure E10. The coil of copper wire is the unknown resistor P.

2   Place the coil, as shown in figure E 10, in a beaker containing ice and water.

3   When the coil has reached the temperature of melting ice, find the balance point of the bridge.
Note. The value of Q should be such that the balance point J is near to the centre of the wire.

4   Measure and record the balance lengths AJ and JB.

5   Interchange P and Q and repeat the measurement. Find the average balance lengths and hence the resistance of the coil.

6   Warm the water about 10 °C. Keeping its temperature steady, repeat steps 4 and 5 to determine the resistance of the coil at this temperature. Record the exact value of the temperature.

7   Repeat step 6 for a series of values of temperature up to 100 °C.

8   Plot a graph of the resistance of the coil (y-axis) against the temperature (x-axis).

9   Use your graph to determine a value for the temperature coefficient of resistance.
Note. If ice was not available, you can find the value of the resistance at 0 °C from the graph.

10   Estimate the percentage error in your value for the temperature coefficient of resistance.

11   Does your graph give any evidence that the relation between resistance and temperature may not be linear? Explain.

Experiment EP11 Movement of ions in an electric field

Aim

In this experiment you will investigate the mobility of ions. You will see that they move under the influence of an electric field, certain ions moving in one direction while others move in the opposite direction.

Apparatus

copper sulphate crystals
potassium permanganate crystals
ammonium hydroxide solution
filter paper
microscope slide
2 large pins
2 crocodile clips
h.t. power supply
leads
stop clock or watch

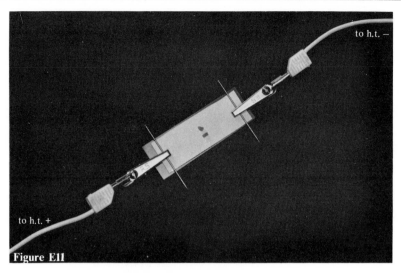

to h.t. —

to h.t. +

Figure E11

1   Set up the apparatus as shown in figure E11.

2   Soak the filter paper with the ammonium hydroxide solution. Make certain that it is not flooded.

3   Place a small crystal of each kind at the centre of the filter paper.

4   Set the h.t. power supply at about 200 V, switch on the power supply and start the stop watch.
Safety note. Do *not* handle the rest of the apparatus with the power supply switched on.

5   What happens to the crystals when the power supply is switched on?

6   Assuming that the colours are due to the presence of ions, what can be deduced about the charge and movement of the purple manganate(VII) (permanganate) ions and the blue tetraamminecopper(II) (cuprammonium) ions?

7   What can you deduce about the speed of the ions as compared to the speed at which the electric field is established through the liquid?

8   Note the distances travelled in a chosen time, and estimate the speeds of the positive and negative ions.

Experiment EP12 Current-p.d. relationship for electrolytes (optional)

Aim

The aim of this experiment is to investigate the relationship between applied p.d. and current for electrolytes.

Apparatus

- ammeter, 0–1 A
- milliammeter, 0–50 mA
- voltmeter, 0–5 V
- copper voltameter with 2 copper electrodes
- copper sulphate solution
- l.t. variable power supply
- variable resistor, 0–15 Ω
- leads
- Hoffman voltameter fitted with platinum or carbon electrodes
- acidified water

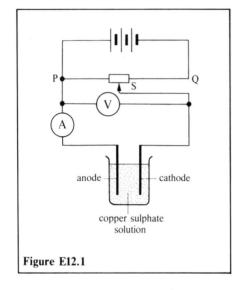

Figure E12.1

Copper sulphate using copper electrodes

1   Connect the circuit as shown in figure E12.1.

2   Starting with the sliding contact S near the end P of the variable resistor, adjust the position of S until a suitable p.d. is recorded on the voltmeter and record the reading on the ammeter.

3   By adjusting the position of S, obtain a series of readings for the current as the p.d. applied across the voltameter is increased.

4   Plot a graph of the current (*y*-axis) against the applied p.d. (*x*-axis).

5   Calculate a value for the resistance of the electrolyte.

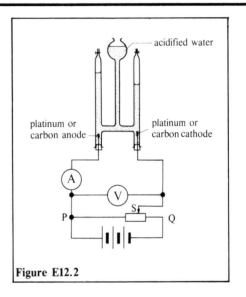

Figure E12.2

Dilute solution of sulphuric acid using platinum electrodes

1   Connect up the circuit as shown in figure E12.2.

2   By adjusting the position of S, obtain a series of values for the current and applied p.d.

3   Plot a graph of the current (*y*-axis) against the applied p.d. (*x*-axis)

4   Use your graph to find the value of the p.d. which must be applied before there is a passage of current.

5   Comment on the features of your two graphs.

Experiment EP13
Current-p.d. relationship for a gas (optional)

Aim
In this experiment you will investigate the conduction of electricity through neon gas.

Apparatus
h.t. power supply
voltmeter, 0–300 V
milliammeter, 0–100 mA
leads
neon lamp
lamp holder

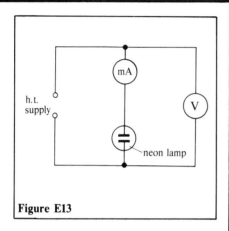

Figure E13

Connect up the circuit as shown in figure E13.

Increase the potential difference from 0 to 250 V in steps. Record both the current and the potential difference each time.

Plot a graph of current I (y-axis) against potential difference (x-axis).

Comment on the shape of the graph.

Experiment EP14
Characteristics of a junction diode

Aim
The aim of this experiment is to find out how the current through a junction diode depends upon the applied potential difference.

Apparatus
- p–n junction diode
- milliammeter, 0–100 mA
- microammeter, 0–50 μA
- voltmeter, 0–10 V
- 6 1.5 V dry cells and cell holder
- variable resistor, 0–2 kΩ
- clip component holder
- leads

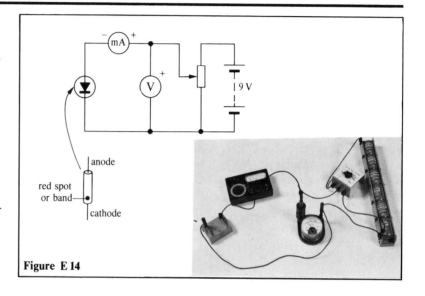

Figure E 14

1 Connect up the circuit as shown in figure E14.
Note. The positive terminal of the battery is connected to the anode (p-type) of the junction. This method of connection is known as forward bias.

2 By adjusting the variable resistor, apply an increasing p.d. across the diode. Obtain and record a series of values of the forward current I and the forward p.d. V.

3 Now reverse the battery connections and replace the milliammeter with the microammeter. The diode is now said to be reverse biased.

4 Obtain a series of values for the reverse current and the reverse p.d.

5 Plot a graph of the current (y-axis) and p.d. (x-axis).

6 Comment on the features of your graph.

Experiment EP15 Principle of the transistor

Aim
In this experiment you will find out how the current in the collector circuit depends upon the current in the base circuit.

Apparatus
- $n-p-n$ transistor
- 6 1.5 V dry cells and cell holder
- 3 1.5 V dry cells and cell holder
- leads
- microammeter, 0–50 μA
- milliammeter, 0–10 mA
- 2 lamps, 6 V
- fixed resistors, 2.2 kΩ, 3.9 kΩ and 10.0 kΩ
- clip component holders

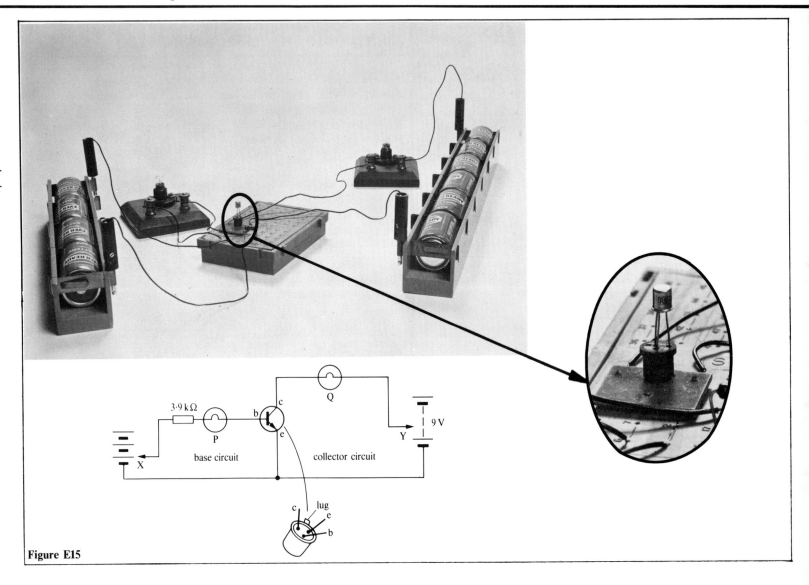

Figure E15

When is there a current through the collector circuit?

Connect up the collector circuit as shown in figure E15, with the flying lead marked Y connected so that there is a p.d. of 6.0 V between the collector and emitter. (Do not connect the base circuit yet.)

Note. Make certain that you can identify the base, emitter and collector. The collector is connected via the lamp to the positive terminal of the battery and the emitter is connected to the negative terminal. The transistor may be damaged if the battery connections in the collector-emitter circuit are interchanged. Remember this in all your work using this type of transistor.

Does the lamp Q in the collector circuit light?

Now connect up the base circuit with the flying lead marked X connected so that there is a p.d. of 1.5 V between the base and the emitter. Notice the effect on the lamps.

Does the lamp P in the base circuit light?

Is there any current through the lamp in the collector circuit?

Maybe the lamp P is faulty. Interchange the lamps and note the result.

From your observations you should have seen that lamp Q will light up only when the base circuit is connected. It therefore seems that there might be a current through the base circuit. To test this, connect a microammeter in series with lamp P in the base circuit.

Is there a deflection on the meter? What does this indicate? How does the size of the base current compare with the size of the collector current?

How can the size of the collector current be altered?

1   With the microammeter in series with the lamp P in the base circuit and a milliammeter in series with lamp Q in the collector circuit, increase the p.d. in the base circuit to 3.0 V and then to 4.5 V (by moving the lead X).

2   Does this have any effect on the current in the collector circuit? What do you notice about the change in the size of the base current compared with the change in the collector current?

3   Connect X so that the p.d. applied to the base circuit is 3.0 V. Increase the p.d. applied to the collector circuit from 6.0 V to 7.5 V and then to 9.0 V (by moving lead Y).

4   What happens to the brightness of lamp Q? Is there any change in the current in the collector circuit? If so, what can you say about it?

5   Connect the flying lead Y so that the collector p.d. is 6.0 V and record the readings on the meters.

6   Vary the resistance in the base circuit by replacing the 3.9 kΩ resistor by one of 2.2 kΩ and then 10.0 kΩ. Record the meter readings each time.

7   How does the change in resistance in the base circuit affect the collector current? What do you notice about the change in the size of the base current compared with the change in the size of the collector current?

8   Make a brief summary of the findings from this experiment.

Experiment EP16 Characteristics of an *n-p-n* transistor

Aim

In this experiment you will examine the relationship between the collector current, the base current and the potential difference between the collector and the emitter.

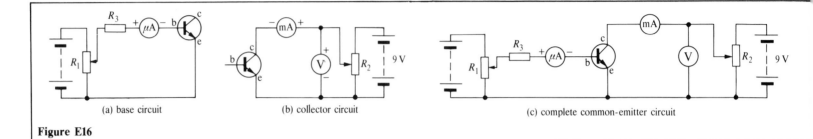

(a) base circuit   (b) collector circuit   (c) complete common-emitter circuit

Figure E16

Apparatus

- *n–p–n* transistor
- 2 sets of 6 1.5 V dry cells and cell holders
- milliammeter 0–50 mA
- microammeter 0–50 μA
- voltmeter (high resistance), 0–10 V
- 2 variable resistors, 0–5 kΩ
- fixed resistor, 2.2 kΩ
- leads
- clip component holder

1   Connect up the circuit by following the sequence shown in figure E16. (If you have not used a transistor before, make certain that you can identify the base, emitter and collector.)
Note 1: the base circuit. The high resistance resistor R_3 is included to limit the value of the base current to the recommended maximum value (as given in the manufacturer's specification).
Note 2: the collector circuit. Make sure that the *positive* terminal of the battery is connected (via the potentiometer R_2 and the milliammeter) to the *collector*.

2   By means of the potentiometer R_1 (which varies the p.d. between base and emitter), adjust the value of the base current I_b to a low value (for example, about 10% of the recommended maximum).

3   By adjusting the potentiometer R_2 (which varies the p.d. between collector and emitter), apply a small p.d. and record the collector current I_c shown by the milliammeter.

4   Obtain a series of values for the collector current I_c and the p.d. V_{ce} between the collector and emitter. (Start with small increases in V_{ce}.)
Note. The value of the base current may be slightly altered by variations in V_{ce} and must be kept at its selected value while you are taking the readings by adjusting R_1.

5   Vary the base current and repeat steps 3 and 4 to obtain a set of readings for I_c and V_{ce} for different values of the base current I_b.

6   Record your observations in a suitable table.

7   Plot a graph of the collector current (*y*-axis) against the collector-emitter potential difference (*x*-axis) for each value of base current. These curves are known as the *collector* or *output* characteristics of the transistor.

8   For a fixed value of I_b, how does V_{ce} affect the collector current?

9   Use your results to plot a graph to show how the collector current varies with the base current for a fixed value of V_{ce}. Choose a value of V_{ce} within the linear part of the collector characteristics. This graph shows the *transfer* characteristic of the transistor.

10   How does a small change in the base current affect the collector current?

11   From the transfer characteristic, calculate a value for the small signal forward current transfer ratio h_{fe}

$$h_{fe} = \frac{\Delta I_c}{\Delta I_b} \text{ at a fixed value of } V_{ce},$$

where ΔI_b is a small change in the base current and ΔI_c is the corresponding change in the collector current.

Experiment EP17 Transistor amplifier

Aim

The aim of this experiment is to construct a simple single-stage transistor amplifier. You will also measure the voltage gain of the circuit and examine the output p.d. using an oscilloscope.

Apparatus

$n-p-n$ transistor
2 variable resistors, $0-100$ kΩ and $0-1$ MΩ
2 fixed resistors, 3.9 kΩ and 10 kΩ
2 capacitors, 10 μF
microphone
earphones
4 1.5 V dry cells and cell holder
voltmeter, $0-10$ V
signal generator
cathode ray oscilloscope
leads

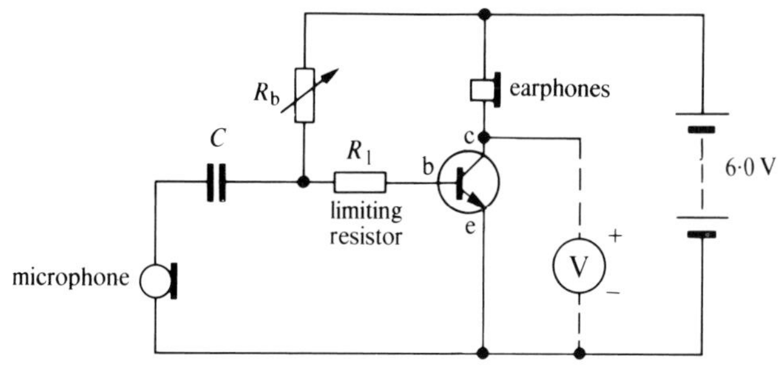

Figure E17.1

1   Connect the circuit as shown in figure E 17.1.
Notes. (a) Ensure that the *positive* terminal of the supply battery is connected through the earphones to the *collector*.
(b) Ensure that you have connected the limiting resistor R_1 in the base circuit.

2   Connect a voltmeter between the collector and emitter as shown by the dotted line in figure E 17.1.

3   Adjust the value of the bias resistance R_b until the reading on the voltmeter is half the supply p.d. (for the circuit shown it should be 3 V).

4   Now speak into the microphone, or tap it. Listen into the earphones. Did you hear a sound?
Note. If you do not hear a sound in the earphones, first check the circuit and then vary the bias resistance. If it still doesn't work, seek help – you may have a faulty transistor.

5   Replace the microphone with a signal generator. Set the frequency at 100 Hz. Switch on and gradually increase the output of the signal generator. You should hear a sound in the earphones. Vary the frequency.

6   Replace the earphone with a load resistor (3.9 kΩ) and adjust the value of R_b until the reading on the voltmeter is 3.0 V (or half the supply p.d.).
Note. The values of load resistance and bias resistance can be calculated from the transfer characteristic of the transistor (the results from experiment EP 16 can be used if you have the same transistor). Find the centre of the linear part of the transfer characteristic and determine the bias current I_b and the corresponding value of I_c.
Calculate the load resistance R using the relationship
$$V = V_{ce} + I_c R,$$
where V is the p.d. across the terminals of the supply and V_{ce} is the collector potential (for example 3.0 V).
Calculate the bias resistance R_b using the relationship
$$V = I_b R_b.$$
You can assume that the p.d. across the bias resistor is equal to the supply p.d. The p.d. between the base and emitter is very small (about 0.6 V).

Turn over ➡

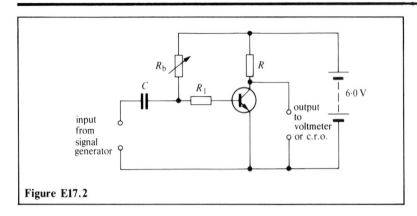

input from signal generator

6·0 V

output to voltmeter or c.r.o.

Figure E17.2

EXTENSION

A two stage amplifier

1   Construct a second amplifier.

2   Connect the output of the first stage amplifier to the input of the second stage amplifier (via a coupling capacitor of value 10–25 μF).

3   Use the c.r.o. to estimate the voltage gain of the two stage amplifier.

7   Set the frequency of the signal generator at 100 Hz. Use the c.r.o. to monitor the output from the circuit, as shown in figure E 17.2. Switch on the time base and adjust the controls until you have a waveform on the screen.

8   Find out what happens to the shape of the waveform
(a) as the input p.d. is gradually increased,
(b) as the bias current is varied.

9   Adjust the bias current so that the waveform on the screen is free from distortion, for a small input p.d.

10   Use the c.r.o. to measure the input p.d. V_i and the output p.d. V_o.

11   Calculate the voltage gain of the circuit.

Aim

In this experiment you will find out the relationship between the input p.d. and output p.d. of a transistor circuit.

Apparatus

$n-p-n$ transistor
fixed resistors, 2.2 kΩ and 15 kΩ
6 1.5 V dry cells and cell holder
variable resistor, 0–5 kΩ
2 voltmeters, 0–10 V
leads

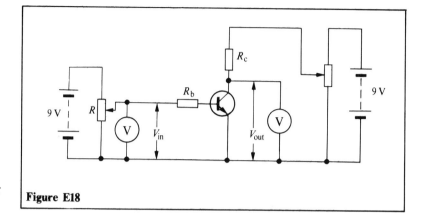

Figure E18

1 Connect the circuit as shown in figure E 18.

2 By adjusting the variable resistor R, obtain a series of values for the input and output p.d.s.

3 Plot a graph of the output p.d. (y-axis) against the input p.d. (x-axis).

4 Comment on the features of your graph.

5 Explain how the circuit enables the transistor to behave as a switch.

Answers

Chapter 1

1.1   Magnetic, chemical and thermal (heating) effects.

1.3   Because an electron has a negative charge.

1.4 6.25×10^{18} electrons, that is, $\dfrac{1}{1.6 \times 10^{-19}}$ electrons.

1.6   (a) 6000 s.
(b) 2×10^{19} electrons.

1.8   (a) 1 kg contains $\dfrac{6.0 \times 10^{26}}{63.5}$ atoms, 1 m³ of copper has a mass of 9×10^3 kg. Number of atoms in 1 m³
$$= \frac{6.0 \times 10^{26}}{63.5} \times 9 \times 10^3$$
$$\approx 10^{29}$$
(b) Using the equation $v = I/(nAe)$,
$$v = \frac{1}{10^{29} \times 10^{-6} \times 1.6 \times 10^{-19}} \text{ m s}^{-1}$$
$$\approx 10^4 \text{ m s}^{-1}$$

1.9   The electromotive force of a source can be defined as the energy converted into electrical energy when unit charge passes through it.

The term electromotive force can be misleading, because e.m.f. measures energy per unit charge, not force. However, the source of e.m.f. is responsible for moving charge around the circuit.

Alternatively, we can define the e.m.f. of a source as the work done on unit charge when it passes through the source.

1.10 $W = EQ$.

1.11   (a) 30 J.
(b) 120 J.

1.12   1 728 000 J.
$W = 12 \times 40 \times 3600$ J.

1.14   (a) $W = VQ$.
(b) 16 V.

1.15   The current is *proportional* to the potential difference.

1.17   192 V.
Either
total resistance = 500 Ω
current $= \dfrac{240}{500}$ A,
p.d. across 400 Ω resistor $= \dfrac{240}{500} \times 400$ V.
or
p.d. across 400 Ω resistor $= \dfrac{4}{5}$ of total p.d.
$$= \frac{4}{5} \times 240 \text{ V}.$$

1.20   Series 12 Ω, parallel 1.09 Ω.

1.21   5.75 Ω.

1.22   D: that is, the resistance will decrease by a factor of 2. This is because

l is increased by a factor of 2 and A is increased by a factor of 4 and $R \propto l/A$.

1.24   8.0 m.
Using $R = \rho l/A$, $R = \dfrac{5.0 \times 10^{-7} \ \Omega \text{ m} \times l}{0.80 \times 10^{-6} \text{ m}^2}$
therefore $l = \dfrac{5.0 \times 0.80 \times 10^{-6}}{5.0 \times 10^{-7}}$ m
$= 8.0$ m.

1.28   38.9 Ω.
$R_{100} = R_0 (1 + 4.0 \times 10^{-3} \ °C^{-1} \times 100 \ °C)$
$R_{20} = R_0 (1 + 4.0 \times 10^{-3} \ °C^{-1} \times 20 \ °C)$
$\dfrac{R_{100}}{R_{20}} = \dfrac{(1 + 4.0 \times 10^{-3} \times 100)}{(1 + 4.0 \times 10^{-3} \times 20)}$
$R_{100} = \dfrac{1.4}{1.08} \times 30 \ \Omega = 38.9 \ \Omega.$

1.29   Graph A. The resistance is variable: it increases as the p.d. increases. The device could be a tungsten filament, which is hotter at higher p.d.
Graph B. The resistance is constant. The device might be a metallic conductor at constant temperature.
Graph C. The resistance is variable: it decreases as the p.d. increases. The device might be made of carbon or a semi-conducting material, which becomes hotter at higher p.d.

1.30   (a) 6.0 V
(b) 2.0 V
(c) 12.0 Ω
(d) 0.5 A

(e) 5.0 V
(f) 10 C
(g) 60 J
(h) 50 J
There is a difference in p.d. of 1 V, owing to the resistance of the supply. 10 joules of energy are dissipated in the supply.

1.31   (a) Energy supplied by battery $= EQ$, energy dissipated in external circuit $= VQ$.
(b) Assuming conservation of energy,
$$EQ = VQ + vQ$$
$$E = V + v$$
The e.m.f. of the supply is equal to the sum of the p.d. across the external resistance and the p.d. across the internal resistance. (V is sometimes referred to as the 'useful volts' and v as the 'lost volts'.)
(c) Substituting for V and v in the equation above, $E = IR + Ir$.

1.32   1.67 Ω.
P.d. across internal resistance = 0.5 Ω, internal resistance = 0.5/0.3 Ω = 1.67 Ω.

1.33   (a) $E = V$ if the internal resistance of the supply is zero, or when there is no current through the circuit.
(b) The p.d. is half the e.m.f. when the external resistance equals the internal resistance.

1.34 (a) 1.0 A.
E.m.f. of battery = 9.0 V,
external resistance = 1.5 Ω,
internal resistance = 3.0 Ω,
total resistance = 4.5 Ω,

current in circuit = $\frac{9.0}{4.5}$ A = 2.0 A,

current through each resistor = 1.0 A.
(b) 3.0 V.
P.d. across terminals of battery is given
by $V = 2 \times 1.5$ V, or $V = 1 \times 3$ V.

1.35 E.m.f. of accumulator = 2.1 V,
internal resistance = 0.8 Ω.
In the charging circuit,
$\qquad 2.5$ V $- E = 0.5$ A $\times r$
where E and r are the e.m.f. and the
internal resistance respectively.
In the discharging circuit,
$\qquad E = 0.25$ A $(7.6 \ \Omega + r)$.

1.36 A watt is equal to an energy transfer
rate of one joule every second, that is
1 W $= 1$ J s^{-1}.

1.37 (a) 10 V
(b) 20 C
(c) 200 J
(d) 20 W

1.39 3 600 000 J.
1 kilowatt hour = 1000 W $\times$ 3600 s
$\qquad\qquad\qquad = 3\ 600\ 000$ J.

1.40 (a) Resistance of bulb in use
= 960 Ω. The normal operating temperature (2000 K) is far above room
temperature. The student measured the
resistance of the filament at room
temperature, not at its operating
temperature.
(b) 0.8 W.

Current through resistor = $\frac{4 \times 10^3}{20 \times 10^6}$ A.

Power dissipated = $\frac{4 \times 10^3}{20 \times 10^6} \times 4 \times 10^3$ W
$\qquad\qquad\qquad = 0.8$ W
(c) Possible estimated values may be:
circuit resistance = 2 Ω,
current = 0.75 A,
life (time) = 10 hours = 36 000 s.
Energy stored in one dry cell
$\qquad\qquad = 1.5 \times 0.75 \times 36\,000$ J
$\qquad\qquad \approx 40\,000$ J.
Number of dry cells needed to provide
4 000 000 J (approximately 1 kW h) = 100.
If each cell costs 20p, the cost of 1 kW h
of energy from dry cells is about £20.
1 kW h supplied from the mains costs
about 2.5p.
Note: this question asks for an estimate,
so any answer that is fairly near to these
figures would be acceptable.

1.41 (b) EIt represents the energy
supplied, VIt the energy dissipated in the
load, and I^2rt the energy dissipated in the
source.

1.44 For $R = 20 \ \Omega$,
$I = 0.57$ A, $V = 11.43$ V, $P = 6.5$i W.
For $R = 400 \ \Omega$,
$I = 0.30$ A, $V = 120$ V, $P = 36$ W.
For $R = 8000 \ \Omega$,
$I = 0.029$ A, $V = 229$ V, $P = 6.53$ W.
The significance that can be attached to
these results depends on the purpose for
which the load is connected to the source.
If a high p.d. is required, then the resistance of the load must be as high as
possible. If the maximum possible power
to the load is required, then the best value
for its resistance is 400 Ω. The power is
then a maximum because the load resistance is equal to the resistance of the
source.

1.47 (a) $I_1 = 1.0$ A, $I_2 = 1.0$ A, $I_3 = 0.0$ A.
Applying Kirchoff's rules to the circuit,
$I_2 = I_1 + I_3$
6 V $= (2 \ \Omega \times I_1) + (4 \ \Omega \times I_2)$
4 V $= (6 \ \Omega \times I_3) + (4 \ \Omega \times I_2)$.
To solve these equations, first substitute
for I_2 in the last two equations, then
eliminate I_1 (or I_3).
(b) With battery E_2 reversed,
$I_1 = 1.73$ A, $I_2 = 0.64$ A, $I_3 = -1.09$ A.
The negative sign indicates a current in
the opposite direction to that shown in
figure 1.20.

Chapter 2
2.1 Because no current passes through
the galvanometer, when used as a null
indicator, at the important stage.

2.2 10 divisions per microampere.

The current in the circuit = $\frac{2}{2 \times 10^4}$ A
$\qquad\qquad\qquad = 10^{-4}$ A
(The resistance of the galvanometer is
negligible compared to $2 \times 10^4 \ \Omega$.)
Current through galvanometer
$\qquad = \frac{5}{100} \times 10^{-4}$ A
$\qquad = 5 \times 10^{-6}$ A.
Sensitivity $= \frac{50}{5 \times 10^{-6}}$ div per A
$\qquad\qquad = 10$ div per μA.

2.4 An ammeter should have a low
resistance so that it does not cause a large
change in the current that is being
measured: if the resistance is appreciable,
the current to be measured will be
reduced. An ideal ammeter would have
zero resistance.

2.5 If R_s is the shunt resistance,
0.015 A $\times 5 \ \Omega = R_s \times 1.485$ A.
Therefore a resistance of 0.050(5) Ω must
be placed in parallel with the milliammeter.

2.7 A voltmeter should have a high resistance so that it does not cause a large change in the p.d. that is being measured: if the resistance is not high, the current through the meter will be an appreciable fraction of the current in the main circuit, and the p.d. between the points to which the voltmeter is connected will be reduced. An ideal voltmeter would have infinite resistance.

2.8 If a resistance R is placed in series with the galvanometer,
$100 \text{ V} = (R + 5 \ \Omega) \ 2.0 \times 10^{-3} \text{ A}$.
Therefore a resistance of 49 995 Ω, in series, is needed to adapt the galvanometer.

2.9 (a) 20 V across the 500 Ω resistor, and 80 V across the 2000 Ω resistor.
(b) 16.7 V across the 500 Ω resistor, and 66.7 V across the 2000 Ω resistor.
(c) The resistance of the voltmeter is of the same order as the other resistors in the circuit. Connecting the voltmeter increases the current in the circuit, but an appreciable fraction of this current goes through the voltmeter, so the p.d. across the resistors is reduced. To get accurate readings for this circuit, the resistance of the voltmeter should be much higher than 2000 Ω.

2.10 Voltmeters are commonly graded according to their 'resistance per volt' at full-scale deflection. The higher the resistance per volt of the voltmeter, the smaller the current that passes through it and so the smaller the effect on the circuit to which it is connected.
To adapt A_1 to the required range, the resistance of the meter would be 2500 Ω, giving 100 Ω/V.
To adapt A_2 to the required range, the resistance of the meter would be 250 000 Ω, giving 10 000 Ω/V.
A_2 would be the better meter to choose.

2.11 $R_1 = 0.005 \ \Omega$, $R_2 = 0.029 \ \Omega$.
For the 0–1.5 A range,
$0.005 \text{ A} \times 10 \ \Omega = (R_1 + R_2) \times 1.495 \text{ A}$.
For the 0–10 A range,
$0.005 \text{ A} \times (10 \ \Omega + R_2) = R_1 \times 9.995 \text{ A}$.

2.15 See figure 2.27.

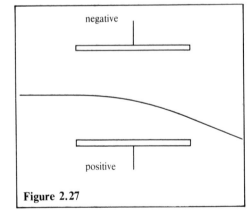

negative

positive

Figure 2.27

2.16 (a) The sensitivity (that is, the deflection per volt) tells us how much the spot is deflected when a p.d. of 1 V is applied across the plates.
(b) When a p.d. of 1 V is applied across the Y-plates, the spot is deflected through a vertical distance of 0.2 cm. The setting 0.5 V cm^{-1} is the most sensitive, because only 0.5 V is required to give a deflection of 1.0 cm.
(c) A vertical line would be observed on the screen. The electron beam is deflected up and down 50 times a second.

2.18 (a) 5.0 V. The length of the line corresponds to the peak-to-peak p.d. The peak value (i.e. zero to peak) is half of this.
(b) 0.75 A.
Peak p.d. across resistor = 150 V,
peak value of current $= \dfrac{150}{200}$ A = 0.75 A.

2.19 200 Hz.
The time t for one cycle = 5 ms,
the frequency $f = \dfrac{1}{t}$
$= \dfrac{1}{5 \times 10^{-3}}$ Hz = 200 Hz.

Alternatively, the spot travels 10 cm in 100 ms, so there are 20 cycles in 100 ms, or 200 cycles in one second.

2.20 Figure 2.28 shows the form of the traces on the screen of the c.r.o.

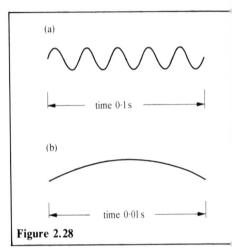

(a)

time 0·1 s

(b)

time 0·01 s

Figure 2.28

(a) Time base frequency = 10 Hz, so the spot takes 0.1 s to sweep across the screen. Frequency of applied p.d. = 50 Hz, so one complete cycle takes 0.02 s.
The trace therefore shows 5 cycles.
(b) Time base frequency = 100 Hz, so the spot takes 0.01 s to sweep across the screen. One cycle of the applied p.d. takes 0.02 s, so the trace shows half a cycle.

2.21 (a) P.d. across battery = 11.0 V, p.d. across R_1 = 7.0 V.
(b) There is a drop in voltage between the terminals of the cell because of the cell's internal resistance:
$E - V = 2 \text{ A} \times 0.5 \ \Omega = 1.0 \text{ V}$.

2.22 0.33 V.

Current through circuit $= \dfrac{1}{27 \times 10^3}$ A

$\qquad\qquad\qquad\quad = 0.33 \times 10^{-3}$ A,

p.d. across 1 kΩ resistor

$\qquad = 0.33 \times 10^{-3} \times 10^3$ V.

Alternatively, p.d. across 1 kΩ resistor is one twenty-seventh of 9.0 V.

2.24 (a) If the resistance per cm varies along the wire (owing to a change in cross-sectional area), then the p.d. will not be proportional to the length.
(b) If the current along the wire changes during a potentiometer experiment, then the p.d. between A and J will also change. A lead–acid accumulator gives a steady current for a long period of time, whereas a dry cell does not. The e.m.f. of a dry cell falls in use, owing to the effect known as *polarisation*.

2.25 (a) Because the p.d. across AJ, $I\sigma l$, must be either greater or less than the applied p.d. for a current to pass through the galvanometer.
(b) No. It is just a convention to place the galvanometer in the sliding-contact part of the circuit under test.

2.26 (a) 150 cm.
(b) C is no longer balanced because the p.d. across the potentiometer wire is smaller; the 1 Ω resistance will reduce the current through the wire. The new p.d.

across the wire is 1.6 V, and the new balance length is 187.5 cm.

2.28 (a) $E_1 = I\sigma l_1$ and $E_2 = I\sigma l_2$

therefore $\dfrac{E_1}{E_2} = \dfrac{I\sigma l_1}{I\sigma l_2} = \dfrac{l_1}{l_2}$

(b) The e.m.f. of the driver cell may not be known precisely, nor its internal resistance and the resistance of the connecting wires. Since the driver cell supplies the current through the potentiometer wire, the p.d. across the wire will differ from the e.m.f. of the driver cell by an unknown amount.
The type of cell chosen for E_2 would be a standard cell (e.g. a Weston cadmium cell) with an accurately known e.m.f.
(c) If the balance point is near B, the percentage error in measuring the balance length is reduced.
(d) Several readings should be taken to ensure that the current through the potentiometer wire is steady. (If a variable resistor is included in the driver circuit, several pairs of balance points can be obtained and an average value of the ratio l_1/l_2 calculated.)
(e) To protect the galvanometer, a series resistor should have a large resistance (of the order of 1000 Ω). A shunt should have a small resistance (of the order of 0.1 Ω). Sometimes a piece of thin connecting wire is used as a shunt.

2.31 (a) $E = I(R + r)$ and $V = IR$, where I is the current through R at the balance point.

Therefore $\dfrac{E}{V} = \dfrac{I(R + r)}{IR} = 1 + \dfrac{r}{R}$

(b) The p.d. across AJ is equal to the p.d. across the cell, on open circuit, so
$\qquad E \propto l_0.$
The p.d. across AJ when the switch is closed is equal to the p.d. V across the terminals of the cell when it maintains a current I through R, so
$\qquad V \propto l.$
The constants of proportionality are equal,

therefore $\dfrac{E}{V} = \dfrac{l_0}{l}.$

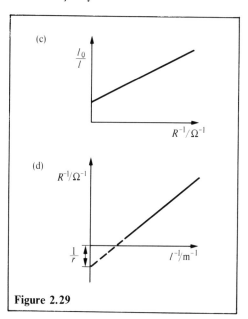

Figure 2.29

(c) Slope of graph $= r$, intercept on vertical (y) axis $= 1$ (figure 2.29).
(d) The equation can be rearranged as

$$\frac{1}{R} = \frac{l_0}{r}\left(\frac{1}{l}\right) - \frac{1}{r}.$$

Slope of graph $= l_0/r$.
Negative intercept on vertical axis $= 1/r$.

2.32 1.00 Ω.
$E \propto 150$ and $V \propto 125$,

therefore $\dfrac{150}{125} = \dfrac{5.00\ \Omega + r}{5.00\ \Omega}$

$\qquad\qquad r = 1.00\ \Omega.$

2.34 $V_1 = IR_1$ and $V_2 = IR_2$
$\qquad V_1 \propto l_1 \qquad\qquad V_2 \propto l_2$

Therefore $\dfrac{R_1}{R_2} = \dfrac{l_1}{l_2}$

2.35 If R was not included, the current through the coil and standard resistor would be of the order of 50 A.
Steps in the equation of S:
(i) draw a circuit diagram;
(ii) current through $R_2 = \dfrac{2\ \text{V}}{20\ \Omega} = 0.1$ A
(the resistances of R_1 and R_2 are negligible compared to 20 Ω);
(iii) p.d. across $R_2 = 0.020\ \Omega \times 0.1$ A $= 0.002$ V (the resistance of R_1 should be the same order of magnitude as R_2);

(iv) current through potentiometer

$$= \frac{0.002\ \text{V}}{40\ \Omega} = 5 \times 10^{-5}\ \text{A}$$

(p.d. across potentiometer should be about 0.002 V to give a balance point near the end of the wire);

(v) value of resistance $S = \dfrac{2\ \text{V}}{5 \times 10^{-5}\ \text{A}}$

$$= 4 \times 10^{4}\ \Omega.$$

Comprehension exercise

1 $\theta_m = 280\ ^\circ\text{C}$.

2 From the graph shown in figure 2.30,

At 255 °C, $s_1 = \dfrac{0.025}{30}$

$$= 8.33 \times 10^{-4}\ \text{mV}\,^\circ\text{C}^{-1}.$$

At 305 °C, $s_2 = \dfrac{-0.035}{30}$

$$= - (11.67 \times 10^{-4})\ \text{mV}\,^\circ\text{C}^{-1}.$$

From equation 2, $a = \dfrac{s}{2(\theta_m - \theta)}$

At 255 °C, $a = \dfrac{8.33 \times 10^{-4}}{2 \times 25}$

$$= 1.67 \times 10^{-5}\ \text{mV}\,^\circ\text{C}^{-2}.$$

At 305 °C, $a = \dfrac{-(11.67 \times 10^{-4})}{2 \times (-25)}\ \text{mV}\,^\circ\text{C}^{-2}$

$$= 2.33 \times 10^{-5}\ \text{mV}\,^\circ\text{C}^{-2}.$$

Mean value of $a = 2.00 \times 10^{-5}\ \text{mV}\,^\circ\text{C}^{-2}.$

3 The graph in figure 2.31 is plotted from the values in the table below.

V/θ in mV $^\circ$C^{-1} $\times 10^{-3}$	θ in °C
6.638	240
6.432	250
6.215	260
6.011	270
5.804	280
5.593	290
5.380	300
5.171	310
4.963	320

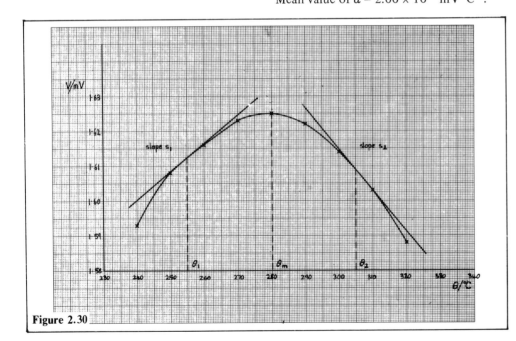

Figure 2.30

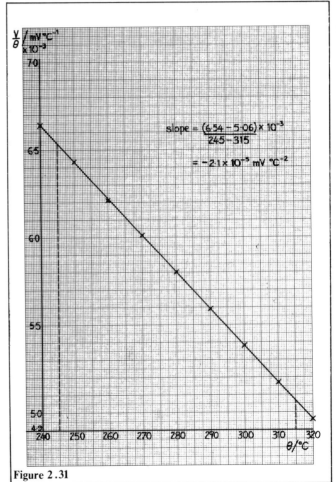

Figure 2.31

From equation 1, $V = a\theta (2\theta_m - \theta)$

$$\frac{V}{\theta} = a (2\theta_m - \theta)$$

Rearranging this equation,

$$\frac{V}{\theta} = - a\theta + 2a\theta_m$$

Comparing with $y = mx + c$, the slope of the graph, β, is equal to $- a$. Therefore $a = 2.1 \times 10^{-5}$ mV °C^{-2}.

In question 2, the accuracy of the value of a depends upon the measurement of the slopes of the tangents – it is the mean of only two values.
In question 3, the slope of the graph was used to obtain a, i.e. an average of all results was obtained.

2.36 The circuit is shown in figure 2.32.

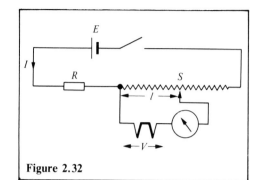

Figure 2.32

(a) $I = \dfrac{E}{R + S}$

(b) P.d. across wire $= \dfrac{E}{R + S} \times S$.

(c) Potential drop per unit length

$$= \frac{E}{(R + S)} \times \frac{S}{L},$$

therefore p.d. across length $l = \dfrac{ES}{R + S} \times \dfrac{l}{L}$.

2.37 0.0061 V.
Let I be the current in the potentiometer circuit, then 1.018 V $= I (1000 \Omega + 24 \Omega)$,

$$I = \frac{1.018}{1024} \text{ A.}$$

If V is the thermoelectric e.m.f.,

$$V = I \times 6.125 \text{ V} = \frac{1.018 \times 6.125}{1024} \text{ V.}$$

2.38 (a) The p.d. across AB is $I_1 P$, the p.d. across AD is $I_2 R$.
(b) At the balance point no current passes through the galvanometer, therefore B

and D are at the same potential.
(c) The p.d. across BC is $I_1 Q$ and the p.d. across DC is $I_2 S$, therefore $I_1 Q = I_2 S$.

(d) $\dfrac{I_1 P}{I_1 Q} = \dfrac{I_2 R}{I_2 S}$

$$\frac{P}{Q} = \frac{R}{S}$$

(e) In figure 2.33, A and C are at the same potential.

$$I_3 P = I_4 Q$$
and $\quad I_3 R = I_4 S$
Thus $\quad P/R = Q/S \quad$ or $\quad P/Q = R/S$
(Note the symmetry in both the circuit and the algebra)

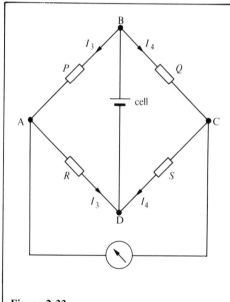

Figure 2.33

2.39 (a) Resistance of network $= 6 \Omega$, current through network $= 1.0$ A (0.5 A through each part),
p.d. across AB $= (4 \Omega \times 0.5$ A) $= 2.0$ V,
p.d. across AD $= (8 \Omega \times 0.5$ A) $= 4.0$ V.
The potential at B is greater than that at D, therefore current would pass through the galvanometer from B to D.
(b) 2.67 Ω, in parallel (for balance, the combined resistance of AD must be 2 Ω).

2.40 Let σ be the resistance per unit length of the wire, then
$$R = \sigma l_1 \quad \text{and} \quad S = \sigma l_2$$
$$\frac{R}{S} = \frac{\sigma l_1}{\sigma l_2} = \frac{l_1}{l_2}$$

2.41 (a) The resistance of the connecting wire is comparable to the resistances that are being compared. Stray resistance (e.g. at terminals) becomes very significant. (A potentiometer method would be more suitable, since the connecting wires carry no current at the balance point.
(b) For resistances of this order of magnitude the galvanometer is not sufficiently sensitive to detect the balance point.

2.43 9.3 Ω.

Chapter 3

3.1 (a) See figure 3.7.

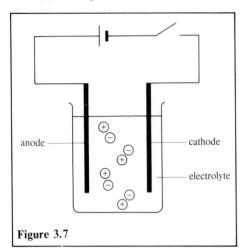

Figure 3.7

(b) The direction of the electric field (that is, the direction in which a positive charge will move) is from the anode to the cathode. The positive ions move towards the negative electrode (cathode). The negative ions move towards the positive electrode (anode).

3.2 At the cathode, each copper ion gains two electrons, to form a copper atom. At the anode, a copper ion is formed leaving the anode with an excess of two electrons. (There is a flow of electrons in the external circuit.)

3.5 If the deposit flakes off very easily, the rate at which the material is being deposited is too great for the area on which it is deposited, so the thickness builds up too quickly. Also, the surface of the cathode may not have been clean enough. A suitable value for the plating current is thus dependent on the surface area of the cathode, and has to be determined by trial and error. A rough guide is to have a current of about 1 A for 50 cm² of cathode surface area.

3.6 During the process of electrolysis a chemical reaction takes place. The net result of the electrolysis of, for example, water which has been slightly acidified is that hydrogen and oxygen are produced. The water has been decomposed (split up).

3.7 (a) 1.1×10^7 C.

$$\text{Charge to produce 1 kg} = \frac{1 \text{ kg}}{9.3 \times 10^{-8} \text{ kg C}^{-1}}$$
$$= 1.1 \times 10^7 \text{ C}.$$

(b) 5.4×10^7 J.
Energy required = $1.1 \times 10^7 \times 5$ J.
(c) 2.75×10^{11} J.
(d) 4.6×10^{11} J.
(e) £3200.

3.8 The Faraday constant is numerically equal to the charge that is required to liberate one mole of singly charged ions in electrolysis.

3.9 (a) 1.52 g of silver is deposited. The silver ion is Ag^+, therefore one mole of electrons is required to deposit one mole of silver atoms.
9.6×10^4 C will deposit 108 g of silver, the charge which passes in 45 minutes
$= 0.5 \times 60 \times 45$ C $= 1350$ C.
This charge will deposit
$$\frac{108 \times 1350}{9.6 \times 10^4} \text{ g of silver}$$
(b) 1.08×10^4 s (3 h).
The tin ion is Sn^{2+}, therefore one mole of tin atoms is deposited by two moles of electrons.
118.7 g of tin requires $2 \times 9.6 \times 10^4$ C,
5.00 g will require $\dfrac{2 \times 9.6 \times 10^4 \times 5}{118.7}$ C.
$$\text{Time} = \frac{2 \times 9.6 \times 10^4 \times 5}{118.7 \times 0.75} \text{ s.}$$

3.10 1.6×10^{-19} C.
One mole of singly charged ions carries a charge of 9.6×10^4 C,
one mole contains 6×10^{23} ions,
charge on a single ion $= \dfrac{9.6 \times 10^4}{6 \times 10^{23}}$ C.

3.13 (a) 24.8 Ω.
The positive terminal of the battery is connected to the positive terminal of the supply. The net e.m.f. is 50 V, so
$$50 \text{ A} = 2 \text{ V} (R + 0.2 \text{ Ω})$$
where R is the series resistance.

(b) 4.0p.
(1.6 kW h at 2.5p per kW h)
50% of the energy supplied is wasted
(49.6% external, 0.4% internal).

3.16 By a flame, ultraviolet light, X-rays or radiation from a radioactive source.

3.18

Substance	Charge carriers
metal	usually free electrons
electrolyte	positive and negative ions
gas	positive ions and electrons

Chapter 4

1 At room temperature an intrinsic semiconductor contains a number of free electrons and positive holes (these are called minority carriers). The number depends upon the temperature and type of material. When a p.d. is applied across the material an electric field is set up which will cause a force to be exerted on the charges. The electrons will tend to drift towards the end of the conductor which is connected to the positive terminal of the supply. Holes will move in the opposite direction.
Note: Germanium has more minority carriers than silicon at the same temperature. This is because less energy is required to create the electron–hole pair.

2 By increasing the temperature of the semiconductor, or by allowing light to fall on the semiconductor. In both cases more electron–hole pairs are created, hence the conductivity will increase (alternatively, we could say the resistivity will decrease).

3 Figure 4.4a shows that the conductivity of germanium increases as the temperature increases.
Figure 4.4b shows that the number of charge carriers increases as the temperature increases.
In both cases, the rate of increase is smaller at higher temperatures.

4.6 The impurity atoms will displace some of the germanium atoms in the crystal. When the trivalent impurity (indium) is added to the intrinsic semiconductor, only three of the existing covalent bonds can be replaced and the vacancy that exists in the fourth bond constitutes a hole. The impurity atoms make available positive charge carriers because they create holes which can accept electrons (valence electrons from a neighbouring bond). The trivalent impurities are known as acceptor or *p*-type impurities – hence, a *p*-type material. When the pentavalent impurity (phosphorus) is added, only four of the five valence electrons will occupy covalent bonds. The fifth electron will be available as a charge carrier. This impurity makes available negative charge carriers because it donates excess electrons. The penta-valent impurities are referred to as donor or *n*-type impurities – hence *n*-type material.
Note: The addition of impurity atoms is known as doping. Doping an intrinsic semiconductor not only increases the conductivity but also serves to produce a conductor in which the charge carriers are either predominantly electrons (*n*-type) or holes (*p*-type). These are called majority carriers.

4.8 (a) The applied p.d. must be greater than a certain value before the diode begins to conduct. When the p.d. is increased, the current increases.
(b) When the applied p.d. is reversed the current is at first negligible, but when the p.d. reaches a certain value there is a sudden increase in the current.
(c) There are two main differences.
(i) The barrier p.d. for silicon is greater than that for germanium, hence a higher forward bias is required before the silicon diode conducts.
(ii) The reverse or leakage current for the silicon diode is smaller and it can withstand a higher reverse p.d.

4.9 (a and b) The applied p.d. produces an electric field which acts in the opposite direction to the electric field which is set up across the *p*–*n* junction by thermal diffusion of electrons and holes. This has the effect of reducing the potential barrier and there will be a movement of charge carriers across the junction in the direction of the applied p.d. As the applied p.d. is increased this movement will increase.
(c) Electrons from the *n*-type material will flow across the junction to the *p*-type. Holes from the *p*-type material will flow in the opposite direction. This movement of charge constitutes the forward current of the *p*–*n* junction.

4.10 The electric field produced by the external source is in the same direction as the electric field in the depletion layer. The potential barrier is increased and the flow of majority charge carriers is prevented.

4.11 The intrinsic material contains minority charge carriers: electrons in the *p*-type, holes in the *n*-type. These charges will experience a force which will push them across the junction. Electrons move from *p*-type to *n*-type and holes move in the opposite direction. This movement of minority charge carriers constitutes the reverse current. It is dependent upon temperature and the type of intrinsic material, because these are the factors which determine the number of minority charge carriers in the material.

4.13 The resistivity of the *n*-type region will be less than that of the *p*-type region. The resistivity of the semiconductor is determined by the number density of available charge carriers. Because the *p*-type region is lightly doped it has fewer charge carriers per unit volume than the *n*-type region.
Note: The mobility (roughly speaking, the ease of movement) of the charge carriers is also a factor, but the different mobility of electrons and holes has a much smaller effect than the different numbers in this case.

4.15 See figure 4.34.

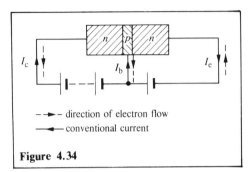

--→- direction of electron flow
←— conventional current

Figure 4.34

4.16 (a) The 'emitter' is given this name because it can be considered to emit electrons.
The 'collector' is given this name because it collects the majority of the electrons that are emitted.
(b) The arrow indicates the direction of the conventional current (opposite to the electron flow, but in the same direction as hole movement).

4.17 The emitter–base junction of the transistor is forward biased: this circuit has a low resistance.
The collector–base junction is reverse biased: this circuit has a high resistance. The action of the transistor is to transfer current from a low-resistance to a high-resistance circuit.

4.18 (a) The emitter is common to the base and collector circuits.
(b) I_e is the emitter current, I_c the collector current, and I_b the base current. V_{be} is the base–emitter p.d. and V_{ce} the collector–emitter p.d.
It is usual to connect the emitter to earth. The emitter will then have zero potential, and is sometimes said to be 'grounded.'

4.19 (a) The value of the collector current depends almost entirely on the base current, which is determined by the p.d. between the base and the emitter, and hardly at all on the collector potential (this is the region beyond the sharp bend or 'knee' of the characteristic).
(b) At low values of the collector potential the collector current falls rapidly to zero.

4.20 The collector characteristics show this because for a fixed collector p.d. (e.g. 4.0 V for this particular transistor), when the base current is changed by 10 μA there is an increase in the collector current of about 1 mA. The transfer characteristic also shows that for a change of 10 μA in the base current there is an increase of about 1 mA in the collector current. (The ratio of the change in collector current to the change in base current gives the small signal forward current transfer ratio, or current gain, of the transistor for a fixed value of collector potential.)

4.21 Because of the action of the transistor – it *transfers* current from a circuit of low resistance to a circuit of high resistance.

4.22 There is no base current until the base potential exceeds a certain value (about 0.5 V). It then increases rapidly. This resembles the curve for a forward biased p–n junction, the only difference being that the current is much smaller. This is because most of the charge carriers cross the junction to the collector. The action is that of a p–n junction with forward bias; when the p.d. between the base and emitter is greater than the barrier potential, electrons will cross the junction.

4.23 The current in the base circuit is very small (of the order of microamperes) and therefore the voltmeter must have a high resistance so that very little of the current goes through it. A moving-coil voltmeter could be used, but a correction must be made for the current through the meter. You could use an electrometer, or d.c. amplifier, which is an instrument which works on a different principle and draws currents of the order of only 10^{-12} A. In this case a correction would not be necessary. The method of connecting the circuit is shown in figure 4.35.

4.24 (a) (i) $I_{c,1}$ (ii) $I_{c,2}$
(b) Increase in collector current is $(I_{c,2} - I_{c,1})$, increase in base current is $(I_{b,2} - I_{b,1})$,
$$h_{fe} = \frac{\text{increase in collector current}}{\text{increase in base current}}.$$

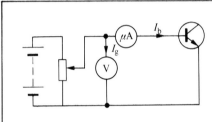

Figure 4.35 The base circuit

4.25 The graph is shown in figure 4.36. Calculate the gradient of the curve at the point where the line AB cuts the curve, then $h_{fe} = \Delta I_c / \Delta I_b$

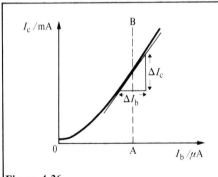

Figure 4.36

4.28 (a) See figure 4.37.
(b) From the graph, ΔI_c = 2.8 mA,
$\quad\quad\quad\quad\quad \Delta I_b$ = 50 μA,

$$h_{fe} = \frac{\Delta I_c}{\Delta I_b} = \frac{2.8}{50 \times 10^{-3}} = 56.$$

(c) 4.5 mA.
(d) If the bias point is 50 μA, the non-linear part of the curve is being used. The output wave form would not be symmetrical.

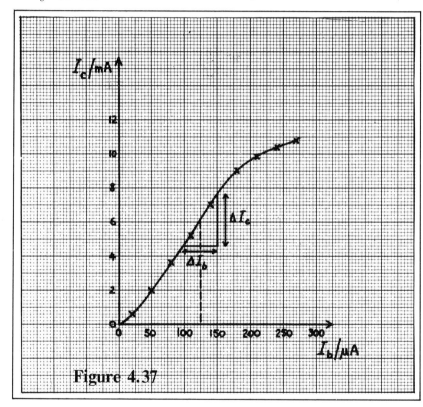

Figure 4.37

4.29 (a) The potential drop across the resistor is $R_c I_c$. Hence, the potential at A is equal to the supply p.d. minus the potential drop across the load resistor.
(b) (i) When the base current increases there is an increase in the collector current. This produces a greater potential drop across the load resistor and the potential at A will fall.
(ii) The potential at A will rise.

4.30 5000 Ω.
I_c = 100 × 10 μA = 10^{-3} A,
4 V = 9 V − R_c × 10^{-3} A.

4.31 The potential drop across the bias resistor is $R_b I_b$.

4.32 0.83 MΩ
0.7 V = 9 V − R_b × 10 × 10^{-6} A.

4.33 The output p.d. is 180° (π rad) out of phase with the input p.d., that is, one is a maximum when the other is a minimum.

4.34 The potential at A may be regarded as a steady p.d. (the steady value of V_{ce} for steady bias current) on which is super-imposed an alternating p.d. Only the alternating component is required at the output. The effect of connecting the collector to the base of a second transistor would mean that the potential of the base would be too high, that is, the base would be incorrectly biased.

4.36 (a) The photoconductive cell has a very high resistance in the dark. Therefore the current in the base circuit is negligible and there is no current through the collector circuit. As the resistance of R decreases, the base current increases. The transistor 'switches on', and a current passes through the collector circuit and operates the relay.
(b) 54 kΩ.
$h_{FE} = I_c/I_b$,
$I_b = \dfrac{20}{120}$ mA.

Assuming that the p.d. across R = 9 V,

$9 V = R \times \dfrac{20}{120} \times 10^{-3}$ A.

4.40 (a) When the p.d. between the base and emitter (the input p.d.) is less than V_1 there is no current in the base circuit − hence, no collector current. The potential at A is equal to the supply potential.
(b) The input p.d. now produces a relatively large base current and hence a much larger collector current. The potential drop across the load resistor is almost equal to the supply potential, and V_{ce} drops to almost zero.

Abbreviations used in the text

Bennet   Bennet, G.A.G. *Electricity and modern physics.* Edward Arnold, 2nd edition (SI), 1974.

Brown   Brown, R. *Electricity and atomic physics.* Macmillan, 1973.

Duncan FWA   Duncan, T. *Advanced physics: fields, waves and atoms.* John Murray, 1975.

Duncan MM   Duncan, T. *Advanced physics: materials and mechanics.* John Murray, 1973.

Nelkon   Nelkon, M. and Parker, P. *Advanced level physics.* Heinemann, 4th edition (SI), 1977.

Wenham   Wenham, E.J. and others. *Physics: concepts and models.* Addison Wesley, 1972.

Whelan   Whelan, P.M. and Hodgson, M.J. *Essential principles of physics.* John Murray, 1978.

Values of physical constants

Quantity	Symbol	Value
Avogadro constant	N_A	$6.02 \times 10^{23} \text{ mol}^{-1}$
charge of proton or electron	e	$\pm 1.6 \times 10^{-19} \text{ C}$
Faraday constant	F	$9.6 \times 10^4 \text{ C mol}^{-1}$

Standard symbols used in this unit

Symbol	Quantity	Unit	Symbol for unit
G	conductance	seimen	S
A	cross-sectional area	metre squared	m^2
S	current sensitivity	radian per ampere	$rad\,A^{-1}$
v	drift velocity	metre per second	$m\,s^{-1}$
Q, q	electric charge	coulomb	C
e	electric charge on electron	coulomb	C
I	electric current	ampere	A
σ	electrical conductivity	seimen per metre	$S\,m^{-1}$
E	electric field strength	volt per metre	$V\,m^{-1}$
		newton per coulomb	$N\,C^{-1}$
P	electric power	watt	W
W	electrical energy	joule	J
E	electromotive force	volt	V
f	frequency	hertz	Hz
l	length	metre	m
m, M	mass	kilogram	kg
n	number of charge carriers per unit volume (number density)	per metre cubed	m^{-3}
V	potential difference	volt	V
R	resistance	ohm	Ω
r	resistance (internal)	ohm	Ω
ρ	resistivity	ohm metre	$\Omega\,m$
a	temperature coefficient of resistance	per degree Celsius	$°C^{-1}$
θ	temperature (common)	degree Celsius	$°C$
T	temperature (absolute)	kelvin	K
t	time	second	s

Acknowledgments

Thanks are due to the following who have kindly permitted the reproduction of copyright photographs: page 30, Central Electricity Generating Board; page 46, Central Electricity Research Laboratories; page 54, Mullard Ltd.

The article on page 21 first appeared in New Scientist London, the weekly review of Science and Technology. The question on page 43 is reproduced by permission of University of London Examinations Council.

Project team   John Bausor (Director)
                     Leslie Beckett
                     Allan Covell
                     David Davies
                     Martin Hollins

Editor   Mary Davies
Designer   Peter Tucker
Photographers   Martin Sookias and Martin Thornton
Diagrams by Technical Art Services Ltd.

John Murray (Publishers) Ltd.,
50 Albemarle Street,
London W1X 4BD.

in association with

Inner London Education Authority
Learning Materials Service,
Highbury Station Road,
London N1 1SB.

Printed in Great Britain by
Martin's of Berwick.